EVERYWOMAN'S
WHOLEFOOD COOK BOOK

Also by CLIFFORD QUICK

NATURE CURE FOR BRONCHITIS
   AND EMPHYSEMA
NATURE CURE FOR CYSTITIS
NATURE CURE FOR SINUSITIS

EVERYWOMAN'S WHOLEFOOD COOK BOOK

by

VIVIEN QUICK

and

CLIFFORD QUICK
M.Sc., N.D., D.O.

THORSONS PUBLISHERS LIMITED
Wellingborough, Northamptonshire

First published 1974
Second Impression 1976
Third Impression 1978

ISBN 0 7225 0236 2

Typeset by Specialised Offset Services Ltd., Liverpool
and printed by Weatherby Woolnough,
Wellingborough, Northamptonshire

CONTENTS

FOREWORD

Many thousands of intelligent people who are interested in *health* are seeking guidance in the management of their dietary.

Vivien and Clifford Quick have produced a publication which is right up to date for modern living, which will provide guidance in the simplest possible terms to eating both for health and enjoyment. Using this book with its large number of attractive but easy recipes anyone, whether the individual living alone or the busy housewife and mother catering for a family, not forgetting the many men who are interested — particularly the batchelors who have to cater for themselves — will be enabled to plan and provide interesting, varied, well-balanced and economic meals on diet reform lines, even though they may never have had the time or inclination to make a special study of nutritional science.

Among the many to whom *Everywoman's Wholefood Cook Book* may be helpful are the caterers and chefs who are called upon to provide vegetarian, diabetic and other special diets to an ever-increasing proportion of their clientele. It will be no less valuable to busy practitioners, whether of orthodox medicine or of naturopathy, osteopathy, herbalism or other schools of healing, who will find that this book may be recommended to patients, both as a general guide to eating for health and in the planning of therapeutic diets.

This book should appeal to people in all sections of the community, both in Great Britain and in many other countries.

ALBERT RUMFITT, N.D., D.O., M.B.N.O.A.

London, November 1973
Dean of the British College of Naturopathy and Osteopathy.

PREFACE

The growth and expansion of health food stores with the associated interest of the public in wholefoods marks a growing realization of the importance to health of whole, natural foods as compared with the many devitalized, denatured and chemically manipulated foods which are widely offered for sale on the shelves of so many present-day shops and supermarkets. Indeed, following on the rapidly increasing spread of health food stores, whole, natural foods are beginning to appear in some of the multiple stores and supermarkets alongside their other goods.

One now hears less of scathing references to 'food faddists' and 'cranks' compared with a decade or so ago and such is the change in the climate of opinion that in all sections of the community people (including many of the former critics!) are seeking guidance in eating for health as well as pleasure, thus fulfilling nature's dual purpose in providing food for both our nutritive and our social needs.

Food is only one factor in health, but it is a basic and essential factor. For the reader who is seeking to improve his dietary, we hope that this book will provide the greatest possible help. On the other hand, sceptics still exist, and to them we suggest that they may at least be prepared to give the scheme a fair trial. In this way, many sceptics have transformed their ideas in accordance with the unmistakable gain in personal health which has resulted.

Concerning the wider aspects of diet reform, the National Health Service is costing the nation vast sums of money. A leading nutritionist has expressed the opinion that the reform of the nation's dietary habits would effect a great reduction in the burden of sickness on our hospitals and other medical services.

The essential and unique feature of this book is the correlation of the basic principles of nutritional science with an abundance of simple but attractive recipes, thus painlessly bringing science into the kitchen!

It is hoped that everyone with the interest of their own and their family's health at heart will read and apply the ideas incorporated in this book in their day-to-day life. We end with a statement from one who has done so, Bill Pickering, one-time holder of the world swimming record for the English Channel

When I first commenced my long distance swimming over thirty-six years ago I was very fortunate in being introduced to the diet reform way of living. How grateful I am today for that wonderful introduction.

I have always been most successful in all my swims, having held several records including one world record for the English Channel. In 1969, at the age of forty-eight, I set a new record for the Bristol Channel and also became the first and only man in the world to swim across the treacherous Wash.

I have always maintained that my food reform way of living and the helpful advice I received from the authors of this book was a great asset to me. Although readers of *Everywoman's Wholefood Cook Book* may not all wish to swim the Channel, I am confident that they will greatly benefit in health if they carry out its principles.

Elmer, Middleton-on-Sea, Sussex   Vivien and Clifford Quick

WHOLEFOOD COOKERY

The usual reaction to being 'on a diet' is — 'But how dreadfully dull!' It suggests too frequently the compulsion to eat contrary to inclination and without enjoyment — an enforced restriction on the desperately sick, or a slightly heroic and self-denying effort to achieve weight reduction (often supplemented by slimming tablets which 'pep up' initially, only to depress later). It is my aim to dispel this notion.

A century or so ago, cooking in all its branches was considered an art — the art of producing dishes to please the palate and sometimes also the eye. Girls were trained from an early age to regard some knowledge of this art as of great importance — socially to become a good hostess, and in the home life to 'reach a man's heart through his stomach.'

REVOLUTIONARY IDEAS
The twentieth century has brought revolutionary ideas. Firstly, the discoveries of chemistry and physiology have given birth to an expanding science of nutrition. Foods have been classified in various categories — the energy-giving or calorie foods, the protein or body-building foods, etc.

The discovery of vitamins has been given great prominence, and various deficiency diseases have been ascribed to absence or insufficiency of these substances in the diet. More recently, the importance of the so-called mineral salts has been increasingly emphasized.

Orthodox medicine, while taking some account of these discoveries, has to a large extent failed to make use of them in the treatment of disease. This is due partly to the lack of emphasis on dietetics as a therapy in the medical curricula in comparison with treatment with drugs, sera and surgical operations, and also partly to the practical difficulties of giving dietetic instructions in a busy practice to patients who expect the traditional pills or bottle of medicine for their ailments.

NEGATIVE ASPECTS OF NUTRITION

Thus, in the majority of doctors' practices advice on food matters seldom goes beyond the negative aspects of nutrition; certain patients may be advised what they should *not* eat (e.g., 'no bread, sugar or potatoes' for the overweight patient, 'no fat' for the liver and gall-bladder cases, 'no roughage' for the peptic ulcer or colitis sufferer, etc.). Other than this and the general idea that dietary deficiencies may be compensated by the prescription of vitamin pills (largely synthetic) and that anaemia may be controlled by iron pills, most people are left entirely without guidance as to what they should eat for health.

In fact, the great majority do not realize the extent to which health depends on what we eat. It has fallen to other schools of healing, notably the naturopaths, some osteopaths and homoeo-paths and a few health-conscious doctors — mainly those who are vegetarians — to recognize the paramount importance to health of a balanced dietary of whole, natural foods, and to realize that the management of dietary is the main, and often the only, successful way in which many of our present diseases may be treated. By the correct use of nutritional therapy, in fact, it may be possible to eradicate many of the diseases of civilization.

The discoveries of the vitamins and mineral salts present in natural foods fully support the Nature Cure view of the importance of the principle of wholeness — the necessity to see that our diet consists of food in sufficient variety and as near the natural state as possible to ensure the maximum content of all these essential elements and compounds.

There is no doubt that it is primary, natural, whole foods upon which the human race has depended for very many centuries for its existence before the advent of modern technology. There have been many examples of primitive peoples who have maintained a state of physical excellence on such foods which is becoming an increasing rarity as civilization extends to their communities. Among the factors which may affect the subtle but vitally important matter of natural freshness and quality is the insistence on keeping qualities, often termed 'shelf-life'. This keeping quality is increasingly being secured by processing, the use of chemicals, and refrigeration (it is now known that certain dangerous bacteria may survive refrigeration) and, more recently, irradiation of food has been introduced into a number of countries although its effects — certainly its long-term effects — are still problematical.

This book is not primarily concerned with the measures of special diets and curative fasts that are advocated for the treatment of specific disease conditions, the efficacy of which has already been proved by many thousands of sufferers in all parts of the world, but is mainly concerned with advocating a reform of diet as a way of life to those whose ills have been cured by naturopathic methods of therapy, so that they may permanently maintain their improved health, and also to all those who desire to achieve a high standard of health and avoid the diseases of civilization in themselves and their children.

BALANCE IN DIET
The system of sensible eating, or diet reform, goes beyond the mere avoidance of deficiencies. It places great emphasis also on *balance* in diet. Certain foods have been found conducive to the formation of a state of acidosis in the system when eaten in excess. These are the foods that contain a high proportion of carbohydrate or protein.

By reducing intake of such foods and increasing the intake of all those fruits and vegetables which have an alkaline reaction when assimilated, a correct acid-alkali balance can be maintained, and acidosis (or reduced alkalinity) can be avoided.

Other important points are the inclusion in the diet of an adequate proportion of uncooked food, the adoption of methods of cooking that will avoid unnecessary reduction of the value of the food, and also the combination of foods in ways that will render them more easily digestible — a point of particular importance for those whose digestions are not particularly strong.

WORLD SHORTAGES
But the twentieth century has brought other factors into being.

Situations undreamed of by Mrs Beeton have arisen. Two world wars and new economic factors have created world shortages of many foods. These difficulties are presenting big problems to the experts but they may not prove to be so difficult to solve if humanity shows an intelligent desire to adapt itself to changed and changing conditions. In fact, many valuable lessons have been learned from hardship, and it is possible that we may learn to use our food resources more wisely and well for the lasting benefit of the race. This is where we can all play a part, and not merely 'leave it to the experts.'

Another feature of modern times is the impact of commercialism, which seems to hate to leave our food alone. It must try to make it 'purer,' softer, whiter or more attractively coloured, to preserve it or otherwise process, packet or can it. To extract a vitamin from our food and sell it back to us in a packet or bottle, or to substitute a factory-made synthetic product, is a triumph for the manufacturing chemist; but it might be better for us had it been left where nature put it in the first place. Hence our insistence on the need for pure unadulterated, *wholefood*.

Unfortunately, many orthodox nutritionists tend to decry those who advocate whole, unprocessed foods, grown organically — that is, using compost and other forms of natural humus and avoiding the use of chemical fertilizers, poisonous chemical sprays and insecticides.

By some strange reasoning it is considered sensible and scientific to accept food from which valuable nutrients have been removed in order to improve keeping qualities and to risk ingesting antibiotics and other chemicals which have been added for similar reasons. Also, apparently, according to the same authorities, it is more 'sensible' to accept our foods chemically coloured, flavoured or otherwise artificially 'improved,' even though many such processes have been shown already to be harmful to health. It is true to say that the effect of such tampering with food has never been thoroughly investigated, but such evidence as has been provided by Dr Franklin Bicknell, in his book, *Chemicals in Food*, (Faber & Faber), supports emphatically our claim that by exercising a preference for whole, unprocessed foods we are taking the safe course, and we may be certain that such foods are better for health in every way. Also, the reports to date on the research project known as the 'Haughley Experiment,' and sponsored by the Soil Association, are providing further evidence in favour of organically grown wholefoods.

Additional support for our view comes from the writings of Dr Hugh Sinclair, of Oxford, who, referring to modern food processing, has stated, 'the chronic effects . . . on man we do not know because the requisite controlled research has not been done,' but the evidence presented by Dr Sinclair. leaves little room for doubt concerning the harm that is done to health by modern sophisticated foods.

REFINED CARBOHYDRATES AND DISEASE
Further substantial evidence has been presented by three doctors, working in collaboration. (*Diabetes, Coronary Thrombosis and the Saccharine Disease,* by T.L. Cleave, G.D. Campbell and N.S. Painter, published by John Wright, Bristol). Their work established, as a result of studies in the relationship of diet to health in many parts of the world, a connection between the consumption of refined carbohydrates (white flours, cereals and white sugars in the many forms in which they appear in civilized foods) and a number of modern diseases, including diabetes, dental decay, periodontal diseases ('pyorrhoea', etc.), gastric and duodenal ulcers, diseases of the colon (including diverticulosis), varicose veins and femoral thrombosis, haemorrhoids, variocele, coronary thrombosis (an increasingly common cause of sudden death), bowel infections (bacillus-coli, etc.), gall-bladder disease, appendicitis, pyelitis and certain skin diseases.

No doubt further additions could be made to this formidable list.

Health Food Stores are to be found in almost every town today. It is the aim of these stores, and the firms that supply them, to safeguard their customers by ensuring that their products are, as far as possible, in a whole, natural, unadulterated state with their full content of vitamins, minerals, etc., unimpaired. In the course of this book a few proprietary products are mentioned which are specialized with respect to certain important food factors. These are printed in italics.

SENSIBLE FEEDING

These are the main considerations governing the approach to sensible feeding in these modern times. They are based in general on orthodox findings, well established and generally agreed. They can, moreover, be tested and verified by any one of us in our own life. What is advocated is not a 'back to nature' movement in a primitive sense. It is an attempt to adapt intelligently our new knowledge of nutrition, and so avoid the dietetic errors that have been revealed by this knowledge. In his book *Nutrition and National Health* Sir Robert McCarrison — a leading expert — shows that many native tribes suffer in health because of defective diet, whereas those tribes that have a high standard of health owe this largely to having (more by accident than design) what nutritional science recognizes as a good diet.

In spite of the well-established principles of dietetics, there are many who feel that to give any consideration to diet is 'cranky.' They point to Mr Hearty Eater, who breaks all the rules and seems to 'get away with it.' The answer is that he is the exception that proves the rule. Nature has endowed us all with powers of compensation without which our common errors of life would have killed us all long ago; but our individual tolerance varies greatly, so that one can carry on where another breaks down. A close, expert examination of Mr Hearty Eater would probably reveal that he is not such a perfectly healthy specimen as we might suppose, nor is there any certainty that he will not pay the penalty for his error in the not too distant future. Meanwhile, there are vast numbers who realize the importance of diet and are conscious of their own imperfect health, and who are only too glad to be given a lead to a way of life that will result in improved health and a greater enjoyment of life.

We thus return to the original question — must a good diet be dull, or can it be made attractive and interesting? Can delectable food banish uninspired dietary?

To this important question the answer is most definitely yes.

Most dietitians know very little about the culinary art. On the other hand, all too few cooks have taken the trouble to plan their dishes on sound dietetic lines. The object of this book is to show that this gap can be bridged.

We are on the verge of a new culinary era. At one time the demand was for 'good wholesome food.' That still holds good; the difference lies in the fact that the conception of good wholesome food has changed. More people are discovering for themselves that wholesomeness does not lie in stodgy, over-cooked food. Let us have more variety and colour on our tables in the cooking and preparation of the common and not-so-common vegetables.

It will be shown how we can enrich our table by avoiding the untimely death of vitamins in the cooking and the consequent loss of valuable mineral salts.

DIETS OF PRIMITIVE RACES

Civilized diets are deficient in mineral salts and vitamins to an extent not generally realized. Dr Weston A.Price* conducted studies in many parts of the world of the diets of primitive races noted for excellent health and physique. Samples of their foods were taken to America for analysis and were found in every case to be much richer in mineral salts and vitamins than civilized diets. Vitamin content was often as much as ten times greater and mineral salt content comparably as great, some, for instance, being more than 50-fold richer in iron. Can we wonder that anaemia is so common in civilized communities?

Doctors are aware that we suffer from such deficiencies, but their attempts to make good with vitamin pills and inorganic mineral salts is unsatisfactory. There is ample evidence that human beings cannot absorb and utilize satisfactorily minerals from inorganic sources. Artificial vitamins can sometimes produce harmful and even dangerous 'side effects,' indicating their inadequacy as substitutes for the natural products. Natural food is the only satisfactory source of vitamins, minerals and other nutritional factors, known and unknown.

DRUGS DO NOT CURE

The orthodox medical profession and the drug houses between them have instilled into the public an implicit belief in the effectiveness of drugs for the treatment of disease. The truth,

*Nutrition and Physical Degeneration, Weston A. Price. American Academy of Applied Nutrition.

often appearing in medical writings, is that drugs do not *cure*. They may suppress symptoms, and appear to act as substitutes for certain missing biological factors, but they are also causing new diseases ('side-effects') to the extent that leading medical authorities have stated that up to one-third of illnesses for which people are being treated are now due to drugs, including those which are medically prescribed.

Further complications are now added by the widespread use of certain drugs prescribed for anxiety states — anti-depressants or tranquillizers, the monoamine oxidase inhibitors (MAOI for short). These drugs may react dangerously, even fatally, with foods such as cheese, liver, herrings, broad beans, yeast extracts (*Marmite, Bovril, Barmene*, etc.), coffee and alcoholic beverages.

NEW FASHIONS IN EATING

In discussing the relationship between diet and health it is not suggested that other factors — such as negative mental states, worry and overstrain, faulty body mechanics, lack of exercise, occupational factors and other aspects of civilized life, the many errors into which we are all so prone to fall — are not important. These do not fall within the scope of this book, and it suffices to say that, beyond doubt, diet is a principal factor, and therefore any effort to simplify Diet Reform must be of value. If the newer knowledge of nutrition and its practical application were more widely comprehended and practised it could lead to new fashions in eating and thus result in a vast improvement in health, thus greatly reducing the national burden of disease and proportionately reducing the demand for drugs. This book attempts to help readers towards the fulfilment of this need. It is of even more value if the attempt can succeed in enhancing the enjoyment of food by translating dietetic principles into culinary art.

Moreover, the plan presented in this book does not demand the somewhat daunting task of 'Calorie Counting' in order to follow a balanced dietary for weight control and for optimum health and fitness.

SCOPE AND AIMS

The scope of this book is limited by certain considerations. Firstly, the cost and therefore the size of the book is limited so that it shall be available to a wide public. Countless additional recipes could be devised on the same principles. However, if the book shows that modern dietetics can be presented in an attractive, practical form it will have achieved its purpose.

The preparation of flesh foods is not included, a point which will be of primary interest to vegetarians. This does not mean that it may not be of equal interest to non-vegetarians. Many followers of Diet Reform are not vegetarians or vegans, and, conversely, many vegetarians do not follow Diet Reform and frequently suffer from the effects of badly balanced diets. A common error of vegetarian diet is the inclusion of too great a proportion of the carbohydrate foods (starches and sugars), particularly as these are often largely substituted for the omitted flesh foods. There are so many books describing the preparing of flesh foods that those who desire to use these foods can incorporate them in moderate quantities as substitute protein dishes, but bearing in mind that for optimum health Vegetarian Diet Reform is the ideal nutritional plan.

FOOD-POISONING

It should be realized that those who eat meat, fish or poultry are most liable to experience some degree of food-poisoning and possibly other diseases from time to time. Writing in 'The British Vegetarian', July-August, 1971, the nutritional research chemist, Dr Alan Long, Ph.D., A.R.I.C., stated, 'The nation loses more working time from food-poisoning than strikes. Most of the food-poisoning is conveyed in meat from farm animals through diseases known as zoonoses. It manifests in human beings as the squitters, gastro-enteritis, summer 'flu, chill on the stomach, gippy tummy (a reminder of the diarrhoea suffered by military travellers in the First World War); it has caused many hasty operations for "appendicitis" and "brain-tumours", and may bring on symptoms like those of epilepsy.'

The dangers to human health from animal flesh food are increasing with the growing practices of factory farming and the increasing use of drugs both for veterinary treatment and in the addition of hormones and antibiotics to animal feeding stuffs. The vegetable and dairy protein foods are almost entirely free from any such health hazards. In view of the increasing cost of meat, new protein foods which may be regarded as plant meats (e.g., *Protoveg*) are entering traditional markets and to an increasing extent are ousting flesh meats.

Outside Diet Reform circles there is a very widespread and growing interest in the relationship between diet and health, varying from a vague conviction that 'there must be something in it' to a positive desire for more knowledge. To this larger public it is hoped that the book will introduce much increased enjoyment of life — increased enjoyment of health-giving food attractively blended and prepared, resulting in the attainment of a higher standard of vitality and freedom from disease. Furthermore, I hope that many of the recipes will be appreciated on culinary merit.

NUTRITION PART OF THERAPY

For the growing number of practitioners, both non-medical and medical, who regard nutrition as an essential part of therapy, there is an ever-present problem — how to prescribe diet in such a way that the interest of the patient is maintained and his co-operation assured. The patient is apt to feel that he is an unfortunate, cut off from the normal enjoyment of food. Diet instructions in clinical practice are too frequently of a negative nature. The patient is told what *not* to eat, and he may feel a keen sense of being deprived of his favourite foods. The importance of the attitude of the patient to diet is usually best appreciated by the practitioners who try to make their instructions positive (what to eat) instead of negative (what to avoid).

Therefore, any way in which diet can be made more attractive and palatable without detracting from its value must be a definite advantage. The positive attitude must, for the sake of the patient, be extended as a long-term policy to prevent a reversion to the dietetic errors likely to lead to further ill-health. It is well established that enjoyment of food aids digestion. Also, unless certain rules are observed, much of the value of food can be lost by wrong methods of preparation.

In my work as assistant to my husband in his practice as a naturopath and osteopath, I have learned to appreciate the need to offer a solution to these problems.

Patients not only need help in the selection of what they should eat, but also in the preparation of the foods. The help of this nature that can be given in a practice is limited by considerations of time, etc., and not every practitioner or his assistant is a cook. Also, there is the male patient who pleads, 'My wife wants to be helpful but she does not understand this diet business.'

It is, therefore, hoped that practitioners will find that the book supplies a very real need.

TASTE AND HABIT

Likes and dislikes, tastes and habits in food are big factors in relation to diet. Fixed or preconceived ideas often bear little relation to reality and lead many people into serious error. It cannot be too greatly emphasized that our taste in food, our likes and dislikes, can change at any period of life. How do we get these ideas? Frequently one will hear, 'Little Johnnie does not like so-and-so'; on enquiry, it may often be found that little Johnnie has never even tasted 'so-and-so'! The reason for his imagined dislike may be that an adult relative has expressed a dislike for the particular food — children are so imitative — or that the article of food has been presented somehow in an unattractive form, or else accompanied by the anxiety of a fond parent that he should eat it because it is good for him. Either of these reasons can be 'off-putting.'

I have known cases where a child would not touch fruit, and, on enquiry, it was found that one of the parents never ate fruit. The parent claimed that it disagreed with him and either directly or indirectly the idea had been conveyed to the child. The majority of healthy children love raw fruit and vegetables, and this good taste should be encouraged.

While it is true that tastes differ, and even that some people find that certain foods do not suit them (the effect known as allergy), it is even more important to bear in mind that tastes and habits in food need not be fixed for ever. Moreover, it is quite possible to exaggerate the question of allergy. Not merely tastes, but also tolerance to foods, can be changed. For instance, a stomach suffering from hyperacidity due to a diet too rich in carbohydrates may not tolerate acid fruit or green vegetables. Instead of permanent omission of these foods from the diet, it is possible (and indeed necessary for health) to bring the stomach by a graduated diet to a condition where the rejected foods can be not only tolerated but enjoyed.

Admittedly we are creatures of habit, but that does not mean that habits cannot be changed. When it is for our good to change a habit, the effort should be made. It will only be difficult for a time. In a much shorter time than we may imagine it is possible to exchange the old bad habit for the new good one, and the desire to revert to the old habit will vanish. This is especially true of eating habits. The initial effort must be made, but that effort will be assisted if the food is presented in the most attractive possible manner.

DIMINISHED SENSITIVITY

Not only 'tastes,' but also actual taste, can be changed. It is well known that certain small organs (the taste buds) in the tongue enable us to taste food in the mouth. In many people the sensitivity of these organs has been diminished by their eating habits — particularly because, as this faculty declines, there is a tendency to add strong condiments, such as salt, sauces, vinegar, etc., to the food. Also, as many of these victims will be sufferers from catarrhal complaints, the sense of smell will be diminished, and it has been proved that the sense of smell is largely involved in the tasting of our food. Such people may find food tasteless unless it is highly flavoured with condiments. We earnestly recommend them to make a break with their strong flavourings — they are very bad friends. Slowly but surely their sense of taste will improve, and a thousand tastes and scents in food will be reawakened to .add to the pleasures of eating.

Men struggle for wealth — they go to the ends of the earth to seek it; yet if they find wealth but lose health, they lose the greatest prize of all. True health is not found in bottles of medicine, tablets or injections. Its secret lies in the way of life, and its basis is sound nutrition. A little effort to understand and apply the principles involved will be amply repaid — even if it means changing some of our ideas.

LOSS AND GAIN OF WEIGHT

Much has been written concerning 'slimming,' a subject that seems of primary interest to the fair sex with their devotion to the dictates of fashion and desire to appear attractive. Whole series of exercises are recommended; but there is a general recognition that exercise alone is seldom enough without other measures being taken, principally diet and courses of slimming tablets. Frequently there are warnings of the possible dangers of drugs and diets for slimming. Drugs and glandular extracts undoubtedly can be dangerous and lowering to health and vitality. Even worse, a number of them — e.g., the amphetamines — are addictive. Diet for overweight can be perfectly safe if planned on sound lines to avoid deficiencies and maintain balance. The answer is not 'starvation' — the word 'starvation' must not be confused with fasting, which, when properly used, is a valuable therapeutic measure in certain disease conditions — but eating plenty of the right kinds of food in the right proportions. The sugars, fats and starchy foods should be kept to a minimum, and proteins adequate but not excessive; the foods omitted should be replaced by foods rich in vitamins and mineral salts to increase vitality, restore glandular balance, reduce acidity and promote elimination of waste matter from the tissues.

A NEW WAY OF LIFE

Most 'slimming diets' are intended to be only temporary. Our plan for healthy eating is submitted as a new way of life and, with suitable amounts of exercise such a diet will prove not only reducing, but also health-giving and vitalizing. True health should be the aim. When this is attained, superfluous weight will have disappeared, for over-weight in itself is a form of disease. Life insurance statistics prove that a man of 45 who is 25lb. overweight has a reduced life-expectancy of 25%.

The fashionable 'high-protein' diets for slimming are objectionable on the grounds that excessive protein intake imposes a strain on certain vital organs, especially the kidneys.

Furthermore, the same rules with slight variation will enable the over-thin to gain a normal weight. It is not necessary or desirable for abnormally thin people to eat large quantities of the 'fattening' foods. In most cases they already do so. In their case the cleansing, vitalizing foods, the fruits and vegetables (raw in salads, and cooked), will enable their digestive systems to use their food to build sound, healthy tissue. In some cases there may be an initial further loss of weight as the system throws off its impurities. This should not cause discouragement, as such impurities are well lost and improvement of both weight and health will soon follow. Eat for health, and your weight will take care of itself.

THE BASIS OF NUTRITION

Always remember that it is not merely what food you eat that counts, but how you digest it. If you do not feel like eating, do not be afraid of missing a meal — have a fruit or vegetable drink instead (see the section on 'Beverages'). Longer fasts are sometimes indicated, and in more prolonged digestive trouble it is advisable to seek professional advice, preferably from a naturopath and osteopath.

It is good that we should realize the profound effect that mental and emotional conditions exert on our digestion. If you are tense, angry or worried, your gastric secretions from the saliva downwards will be affected, as any physiologist will tell you, and your food will not do you the same good as when you sit down to a meal in a happy, relaxed frame of mind to eat your food with a keen sense of enjoyment. Therefore, let your mealtimes be happy, relaxed and unhurried. If you are short of time, eat less — food swallowed in over-anxious haste may do more harm than good. If you are tired, try to get in at least a few minutes of complete physical relaxation — 'flop out' for a while — before you eat.

The principles of dietetics advocated are, with certain exceptions, to be found in the standard textbooks of physiology. The value of whole foods is emphasized; white flour, polished rice, refined sugars and syrups have been proved lacking in valuable constituents present in the natural products. Losses of these factors in manufacture are the cause of many ills, such as gastric disturbance, constipation and deficiency diseases. Therefore, in place of the more usual ingredients, the use of wholemeal flour, brown sugar, black treacle or molasses, etc., is advocated for all who value health. These wholefoods are obtainable, and increase of public demand would compel manufacturers to produce greater quantities of them instead of the devitalized and deficient products now offered as 'improved' foods. The widespread use of preservatives in food is also deprecated. Too frequently it is good for the manufacturer but bad for the consumer.

GROWING METHODS AFFECT QUALITY
There is an increasing consciousness that methods of growing food can affect its quality and particularly its mineral and vitamin content. The superiority of 'compost grown' vegetables and fruits has been demonstrated by Sir Albert Howard (*Farming and Gardening for Health and Disease*, Faber and Faber) and others, and good work is being done in this direction by the Soil Association whose research projects are fully reported in its official Journal. For those who grow their own fruit and vegetables the compost system is recommended, and it is to be hoped that an increasing number of commercial growers will follow this method as public demand for naturally grown produce increases.

By the selection of a diet consisting mainly of a large variety of fruits, vegetables and dairy produce, an ample supply of the essential vitamins and mineral salts will be assured and the danger of deficiencies avoided.

FALLACY OF HIGH-CALORIE DIETS
The Nature Cure movement has clearly demonstrated the fallacy of high-calorie diets. Provided that generous amounts of fruit and vegetables, raw and cooked, are eaten, the intake of

'calorie' foods — starches, fats and sugars — can be reduced to at least half the amount recommended by orthodox dietetics. The result will be increased efficiency and health, with gain rather than loss of energy. Apart from the fact that a logical theory can be advanced to support this contention, it has been verified in practice by many thousands of people who have tested the matter personally.

This is in accordance with the statement by A. Barbara Callow in her book *Food and Health*: 'To most people, energy means vitality and vigour, and it must be admitted that energy of this kind is concerned far more with such food factors as mineral elements and vitamins than with the calorie value of our food.'

For a moderately active person not more than 20 to 25 per cent. of the total diet should consist of fats, starches and sugars. Individual requirements vary according to age, nature of work, etc.

Investigation of protein requirements shows vast divergence, varying from Voit's 120 grammes per day to Chittenden's value of 60, even for athletes and professional soldiers, and Prof. Hindhede's experiments which gave a value of 32 grammes per day. No reasonable explanation has been given for these vast discrepancies, but a figure of 100 grammes per day has been arbitrarily chosen on the principle of 'rather too much than too little.' We do not accept this. Our experience, based on many thousands of cases, has led us to conclude that Hindhede's figure was not far wrong and even Chittenden's figure somewhat high, always allowing for individual variations. Why should it be assumed that it is quite safe to give diets with excess protein requirements? We maintain that it is just through being forced to deal continuously with excess protein in the diet that the system eventually shows signs of strain. To aim at defining a well-balanced diet and then to advocate excess of a major constituent leads to a diet which is not balanced but over-burdened, and the arbitrary choice of a high figure has no scientific justification.

DANGEROUS HIGH-PROTEIN DIETS

In our balanced diet, the protein foods should not normally exceed 20 per cent. of the total diet. Proteins are regarded as body-building foods although they may also have calorific value.

Individual requirements will again vary somewhat, but even during the 'growing years' high-protein diets are not necessary. There is real danger to health in high-protein diets, particularly when this protein consists mainly of flesh foods. In orthodox dietetics, vegetable proteins have long been regarded as 'second-class proteins', but the standard of health among vegetarians and their many successes in the athletic field do not support this view. Moreover, more recent research has disposed of the 'second class' idea and has confirmed that vegetable proteins from mixed sources are nutritionally 'first class'. Apart from a warning against fried foods, orthodox diet takes little or no account of the effect of food mixtures.

It is our experience in practice that many are not well-informed concerning the protein content of foods. Some guidance is therefore needed to ensure that the proteins in readers' dietary is neither too high nor too low, the latter possibly having more serious disadvantages to health than the former.

Similarly there is much confusion regarding the carbohydrate content of foods. Thus many imagine that crispbreads and starch-reduced breads are 'slimming', when they are not.

For these reasons Tables IV & V are included wherein foods are classified in order of their protein or carbohydrate content.

It should be noted that in addition to the *concentrated* proteins, there are many other foods which have a lesser but nonetheless valuable protein content. Some contain both protein and carbohydrate, and these include certain fruits, vegetables, etc., which contain small amounts of both protein and carbohydrates.

There is need for further investigation here, but common experience tells us that certain mixtures produce feelings of discomfort and flatulence. There is a great deal in favour of food mixtures being reasonably simple, particularly in those whose digestions are not very strong.

SIMPLE-MIXTURES PLAN

In this book the rule has been followed of not eating starchy foods and sugars in the same meal as acid fruit. Here it may be emphasized that, following digestion, starchy foods are acid-forming whereas with the acid fruits the acid is oxidized in the process of normal digestion, leaving a residue of the nutritionally essential minerals which form what is termed the 'alkaline ash'. Sufferers from acidosis who are not used to eating much, if any, acid fruit will be well advised to take only moderate amounts of the more acid fruits at first, meanwhile relying mainly on vegetables which are more alkaline until the normal acid-base balance is nearly restored. Those whose digestions are not strong will find out for themselves the advantages of this simple-mixtures plan which has the further advantage of reducing the total amount of the carbohydrate foods eaten.

Sufferers from diabetes will have no difficulty in selecting low-carbohydrate diets to suit their condition while avoiding deficiencies, thus adding to the interest and variety of their food.

Cooking methods should be such as to preserve the value of the food to the maximum extent. This means the preservation not only of vitamins and minerals but also of flavour and colour. Last, but by no means least, no diet can be satisfactory unless it contains a large proportion of uncooked food. This is one of the greatest sources of error in Western diets. There are some who say we should be better without cooked food. No doubt our remote ancestors lived on raw food before they discovered the art of cooking. Many of us have passed to the other extreme, and seldom or never eat uncooked food. The happy medium is no doubt the answer for most of us. We must learn to think of a salad not as an extra to our summer meal, consisting of a few lettuce leaves and a slice or two of tomato and cucumber, but as an all-the-year round main dish.

The winter salads, with their grated vegetables, can be most attractive, and nothing is more sure to reduce our susceptibility to colds, 'flu and other winter ills. A good plan generally for the two principal meals is that one should be cooked and the other a meal of salad and raw fruit. Sufferers from gastritis and other digestive troubles can introduce uncooked foods gradually and will eventually tolerate them to their lasting benefit.

ALUMINIUM COOKING UTENSILS
The question of the use of aluminium cooking utensils has not yet been satisfactorily settled, but in view of the fact that

aluminium can react chemically with either acids or alkalis and tends to precipitate in the colloidal state, it is probable that good quality enamel, iron or steel utensils are safer for culinary use.

We do not consider that the use of aluminium cooking utensils is advisable.

Experts defending the aluminium industry insist that aluminium is not toxic, but this is not proof that it has no physiological effects. Penicillin was originally considered safe because it was non-toxic, but it is now known that it can produce dangerous reactions. In view of the fact that aluminium can react chemically with either acids or alkalis and so pass into solution from which subsequently it may precipitate in the colloidal state, it is reasonable to assume that iron or stainless steel utensils are the materials of choice for culinary use. Until recently 'good quality' enamelled utensils have also been mentioned as a safe alternative but recent investigations (*The Observer*, London, December 31st 1972), have revealed that one in three of imported casseroles being widely sold in Britain have been found to contain 'disturbingly high levels of the toxic metals lead and cadmium'. This fault is not confined to the cheaper grades. Also, whereas stainless steel utensils will last indefinitely with normal use, enamelled ware is often liable to chip.

In *The Nature of Disease*, (William Heinemann), Dr J.E.R. McDonagh lists medical evidence against aluminium and concludes, 'The authorities concerned with public health would do well to study this evidence, notably the experiments of Professor Tchijevsky of Moscow which constitute a formidable indictment of aluminium as used for culinary purposes.'

Furthermore, we have encountered a number of cases where persistent gastric trouble and also some cases of irritant skin rashes have disappeared after ceasing to use aluminium utensils. Some of these cases have experienced recurrence of symptoms after reverting to aluminium utensils.

Where long boiling is involved, such as in Recipe No. 208, the taste of the product when cooked in aluminium can be readily distinguished from that of the product cooked in stainless steel.

HOW TO USE THE BOOK

In cooking vegetables it is essential to abandon the practice of boiling in quantities of water with soda and salt. This method, so generally used, involves losses of vitamins and mineral salts, the latter being largely thrown away with the water, which is not drinkable and is often objectionable even in its smell.

There is some divergence of opinion on the use of pressure cookers. Some investigators claim that there is more loss of vitamins B and C in pressure cooking, but it has been shown recently that, provided care is taken to ensure that all air in the pressure cooker is replaced by steam before closing the cooker, the losses are not greater than with other methods. In other words, losses are caused by oxidation, which is reduced to a minimum in the absence of air.

Those who do not use pressure cookers can be assured that the method of conservative cooking that we advocate is quite satisfactory (see page 61), and losses both of food value and flavour are minimal.

It will be seen that the recipes are presented in the usual recipe form. Supplemental information regarding mineral salts and vitamins is given in the form of tables at the end of the book.

Table I gives comparative mineral salt and vitamin content of the separate principal items of food. Information has been obtained from standard analytical tables.

Table II indicates those recipes that are good sources of the corresponding mineral salts.

Table III similarly relates vitamin content to recipes.

Tables IV and V provide practical information concerning proteins and carbohydrates.

The sections are classified as protein, starch or starch reduced, etc., to facilitate selection of any type of dish. Appropriate information is given under each section. Dishes containing an appreciable amount of fat are indicated by the letter (F), and those of particular value to sufferers from constipation by the letter (L), to denote laxative value. The majority of the latter owe their laxative action to the presence of a fair amount of bulk and roughage, which provides mechanical stimulation to the musculature of the alimentary tract. This property is common, in varying degrees, to all salads and raw fruit. Laxative value is not indicated in every case, but only where this property is pronounced.

. Acid fruits are indicated by the letter (A), so that those who wish to avoid the mixture of acid and starch may do so. As already explained, contrary to the popular idea, the fresh acid fruits after digestion are *not* acid-forming and do not cause acidity in the system as their end products are alkaline mineral salts. Foods containing sugar are marked (S), in particular to assist diabetics, who must restrict consumption of starches and sugars. All ripe fruits contain certain amounts of fruit sugar, but as fructose (fruit sugar) appears to be tolerated by diabetics, they should not avoid these foods as otherwise their diet will be deficient. Honey also contains fructose.

Calorific values of food are not indicated. We do not recommend high-calorific diets, and we are confident that the selection of a varied and balanced diet from our recipes will ensure sufficient calorific value for all normal requirements. Calorie requirements vary from one individual to another according to age, occupation and activity, as has already been indicated. In any case, the consumption of the higher-calorie foods (fats, starches, sugars and proteins) should be amply balanced with plentiful amounts of the low-calorie fruits and vegetables.

ADDED SALT CREATES HARMFUL EXCESS
The advice we have already given to avoid the practice of using salt and soda in cooking also extends to the use of salt as a condiment at table. In *Biochemistry for Medical Students* (Thorpe), the writer states: 'Salt is ordinarily consumed in amounts greatly in excess of requirement. There is ample in ordinary food without the addition of salt as a condiment.' Salt (sodium chloride), is normally present in most foods naturally in

amounts which are quite adequate. Added salt, either in cooking or at table, potentially creates a harmful excess and it is now medically recognized to the point where the correct treatment for a number of conditions (e.g., heart troubles, kidney diseases, peptic ulcers, hypertension, obesity etc.), includes the adoption of a salt-free dietary.

The recipes are grouped in sections as below. The main dish of a principal meal may be selected from the 'cooked vegetable' section, to which a protein dish may be added, if and as desired, selected from the corresponding section (see specimen menus at the end of the book).

Regarding the need for increased content of mineral salts in our diet, the programme we advocate will ensure considerable advantage as compared with conventional diets, but it should be noted that both Agar-agar and Recipe No. 208 are very rich sources of mineral salts, including valuable trace elements, and therefore care should be taken to include these recipes regularly in the diet. Diet Reform also ensures a good vitamin intake, but, particularly in winter, it may be an advantage to include the juice of a lemon daily to ensure ample vitamin C. Sweeten with honey if desired, not sugar.

Where the term 'white sauce' appears, please note that wholemeal flour and *not* white flour should be used.

Above all, do not regard salads as being suitable and seasonable only in summer, or think that in some mysterious way hot foods 'keep out the cold.' This is a fallacy, for the raw vegetables included in winter salads supply more protective vitamins and are likely to be better and less expensive than summer saladings out of season.

We hope that the variety and interest introduced into the salad section will prove that for all seasons the regular inclusion of salads will be recognized and accepted as being attractive and satisfying as well as nutritionally excellent.

Why is it that many people pay good money for fresh fruit which is ripe for eating, only to destroy much of its food value by cooking? Regrettably, the answer is probably one of attachment to social convention.

Fresh, raw fruit is a 'must' in winter as well as in summer meals.

RECIPES

MAIN DISHES

Salads

The inclusion of grated raw vegetables in salads will be an innovation for many, but they are an essential basis for any salad, particularly winter salads. Although most people soon acquire a liking for grated vegetables (particularly for grated carrot), there are some who at first may find the flavours not quite to their taste. If some grated raw apple and a few chopped dates are mixed with the grated root vegetable, the resulting flavours may be found more interesting. This is particularly the case with raw beet.

Raw parsley and red and green peppers are to be included in many salads. These are very rich in vitamins A and C and mineral salts, and may be included in any or all salads according to taste.

The first four recipes below are for salad dressings, which may be used in moderate quantities. It should be borne in mind that the use of lemon or orange juice or cider vinegar adds acid fruit juice to the corresponding recipe. Those on 'fat free' diet should note that cheeses contain a varying proportion of fat, and, therefore, cheese should be taken in moderate amounts or as prescribed by the practitioner. Dutch cheese contains only about half as much fat as Cheddar cheese, while its protein content is slightly higher.

(1) Yogurt Dressing

One bottle yogurt. Mix in teaspoon honey. Can be flavoured with (a) chopped chives, (b) chopped mint, (c) chopped marjoram, (d) chopped parsley, (e) finely grated onion, (f) paprika.

Yogurt can be used as a dressing just as it is.

(2) Mayonnaise

2 oz. vegetarian margarine or butter.
1 tablespoon flour
2 or 3 tablespoons pieces sugar
1 egg
½ pint milk
½ pint cider vinegar

Melt fat, add flour and mix. Remove from heat, add sugar and beaten egg. Place on gas, and add milk slowly, stirring well to avoid burning. When fairly thick, remove from gas. Allow to cool slightly, then mix in the cider vinegar slowly, stirring all the time. Pour into jars or bottles. Can be kept about 6 days in cool place.

(3) Lemon and Corn Oil Dressing

3½ tablespoons corn oil
1½ tablespoons lemon juice
Any chopped herbs, if liked

Mix oil and juice well and add flavouring. Orange juice may be used instead of lemon.

(4) Egg Mayonnaise

2 egg yolks
Approx. ¾ pint corn oil
3 teaspoons lemon juice (less if preferred)

Beat egg yolks. Add oil drop by drop, stirring evenly. As it thickens, add little lemon juice. Continue adding oil and lemon juice alternately until required taste has been obtained.

(5) *Apple and Celery Salad (A, L)*

Prepare 2 cups of grated or sliced whiteheart cabbage or savoy, and arrange in nest shape on plate. Chop up enough celery to fill a cup ¾ full, and mix with raw grated apple to taste. Place on nest of cabbage.

(6) *Artichoke Salad*

Prepare a cup full of shredded whiteheart cabbage and arrange on plate. If desired, a nest of lettuce leaves can be used instead. Arrange heaps of grated root artichoke round the cabbage, about a cupful altogether. Place a heap of grated raw carrot in centre. Sprinkle chopped parsley over all, and add a few sprigs of watercress.

(7) *Cauliflower Salad*

Prepare a nest of lettuce or watercress. Grate several flowerets of cauliflower and place on nest, placing whole floweret on top. Surround with cucumber slices or radishes shaped like roses.* Sprinkle with paprika and parsley chopped small.

* When the radishes are cleaned, make 4 or 6 cuts across from the root end $\frac{2}{3}$ length of each radish — cuts made at equal angles like an asterisk. Soak radishes in cold water for about 10 minutes, when the cut ends will open out rather like roses.

(8) *Chicory Salad (A)*

Arrange lettuce leaves on plate. Slice the chicory leaves and pile in a ring round the plate on the lettuce. Quarter 2 tomatoes, and arrange on the chicory. Heap a cup of grated carrot in centre. Decorate with parsley.

(9) *Cucumber Salad*

Cut ½ cucumber down the centre, remove the seeds and add them to grated cheese or cream cheese. Mix well with ¼ teaspoon of paprika, and pile into cucumber halves. Cut into lengths of 2 inches, and place 3 or 4 on a bed of lettuce. Arrange tomatoes cut in quarters round plate, and add a few spring onions and sprigs of parsley. If liked, mint or marjoram can be chopped and sprinkled on.

(10) *Dandelion Salad (L)*

Arrange dandelion leaves on plate. (These are inclined to be slightly bitter. If you are lucky enough to have a garden with dandelions, instead of rooting them up as weeds, try blanching them by covering with a flower pot until white, when they will be less bitter and more tender.)

If whole leaves are not liked, line a plate with lettuce, finely chop a few dandelion leaves and sprinkle over the lettuce. Arrange 2 tablespoons of grated carrot in 2 or 3 heaps on the greenery. Add a tablespoon of grated raw beetroot. (The sweetness of the beet helps to counteract the slight bitterness of the dandelion leaves.) Several slices of cucumber arranged round, and 2 nasturtium flowers, which are edible, will add another touch of colour.

(11) *Endive Salad*

Make a nest of endive — the curled type looks attractive. Previously soak a teaspoonful of sultanas in a *very* little hot water. When cold, add them to a heaped tablespoonful of finely grated raw turnip. Heap on endive, and add little heaps of grated raw beetroot and grated carrot. Decorate with mustard and cress.

(12) *Endive and Pear Salad (A)*

Make a nest of endive on plate. Arrange 2 halves of pears with core removed cut side down. Spread cream cheese over the pears so that the skin is covered. Cut one dozen grapes in half, remove pips, and decorate the cheese-covered pears. If liked, a few extra grapes can be placed round the pears. Green grapes could be used on the pears and black ones round them to add to the pleasing appearance.

(13) *Lettuce and Tomato Salad (A)*

Arrange lettuce on plate — at least 5 whole leaves. Take 3 firm tomatoes, cut off tops and remove fleshy insides. Mix with grated cheese, chopped parsley *or* thyme *or* marjoram (only a very little if either of the two last herbs is used). Place in tomato cases and arrange on lettuce. Decorate with sliced cucumber and spring onions.

(14) *Mixed Root Salad with Watercress (L)*

½ cup grated carrot, ½ cup grated parsnip, ½ cup grated root artichokes, ½ cup grated turnip, combined with a tablespoon of sultanas, a tablespoon of grated raw beetroot, finely chopped leek to taste.

Arrange the different vegetables on a plate in little heaps on top of the watercress. If liked, a little paprika can be sprinkled over the salad to make it look more attractive.

(15) *Mixed Summer Salad*

Arrange whole lettuce leaves to cover plate. Place a circle of sliced cucumber round edge of plate. Arrange the following in little heaps inside the cucumber circle: 1 tablespoon raw grated carrot, 1 tablespoon raw grated beetroot, 1 tablespoon raw grated turnip, spring onions to taste. Decorate the whole with chopped parsley or mint.

(16) *Nasturtium Salad (A)*

Arrange nasturtium leaves round plate. Shred some lettuce leaves and heap in centre. Add ½ cup of finely grated carrot and raw beetroot. Place quartered tomatoes round plate, also a few spring onions, and decorate with 2 or 3 nasturtium flowers.
N.B. — Nasturtium is one of the richest known sources of vitamin C.

(17) *Orange Salad — 1 (A)*

2 teacups finely sliced or coarsely grated raw whiteheart cabbage or savoy, 1 large orange. Remove rind and slice orange. Keep a slice or two for decorating top of salad. Chop remainder and add to cabbage. Mix well and serve. If desired, add a little grated orange peel. This can be used as a dessert or as a main dish by adding cheese.

(18) *Orange Salad — 2 (A)*

As No. 17, but add cup of finely grated raw carrot. This adds a decorative touch if placed round the edges of the salad to form a circle.

(19) *Orange Salad — 3 (A) (L)*

Bunch of well-washed and chopped watercress mixed with a large orange which has been peeled and diced. This can be served with finely grated carrot mixed with orange or lemon juice.

(20) Avocado or Alligator Pears

Halve the avocado and remove the stone. Brush over with lemon juice to stop discoloration if the fruit is not to be used immediately. They can be served on a bed of lettuce, watercress or endive — or by themselves. They can also be stuffed in many ways by filling the stone cavity:

1. Chopped hard-boiled egg mixed with a few chopped nuts and salad dressing. 2. Cream or curd cheese mixed with crushed pineapple or chopped walnuts. 3. Lemon and corn oil dressing with chopped herbs (see Recipe 3). 4. Egg mayonnaise (see Recipe 4). 5. Cream cheese and chopped olives. 6. Cream or curd cheese and sliced grapes.

(21) Avocado and Grapefruit Starter

1 large or 2 small
   avocados
1 grapefruit — peeled
   and cut small
Small carton thick
   whipped cream
(A little finely grated
   lemon peel may be
   added to the cream.)

Remove avocado from skin and dice, add to grapefruit and mix in the cream just before serving. Pile into empty skins and serve — or may be served in small dainty individual glass dishes.

(22) Avocado with Cheese and Nuts

Remove avocado from skin and dice. Mix cream or curd cheese well with a little milk or mayonnaise until a very soft consistency has been reached. Mix in a few chopped nuts and grated raw onion or chives to taste.

Pile back in skin or serve in small glass dishes, or place on a bed of lettuce or watercress leaves.

(23) *Avocado Celery and Nuts*

Remove avocado from skin and dice, combine chopped celery to taste and a few grated or chopped nuts. Serve with a dressing (Recipe 3).

(24) *Avocado and Seedless or Seeded Grapes (A)*

Remove avocado stone and peel, brush over with lemon juice to stop discoloration. Place half avocado on bed of lettuce — heap small seedless grapes or seeded big ones into cavity of pear and serve with mayonnaise or the dressing as Recipe 3.

(25) *Avocado Pear and Melon*

Remove stone of avocado and peel. Dice and mix with an equal amount of diced melon. Serve with the dressing as Recipe 3.

(26) *Apple Salad — with Raisins, Sultanas or Currants (A)*

1 tablespoon of dried fruit soaked in orange juice. Then wash a large sweet apple, remove core and chop or grate, mix with a little mayonnaise to stop discoloration — a little chopped celery may also be added. Combine with dried fruit and orange juice and serve on lettuce or grated white cabbage.

(27) *Date and Cream Cheese Salad*

4 oz. cream cheese
2-3 oz. chopped dates
1-2 oz. chopped nuts

Mix cream cheese with milk or mayonnaise to taste, then mix in dates and nuts and lemon juice if desired. Serve on bed of lettuce, watercress or grated cabbage.

(28) *Small Seedless Grape Salads (A)*

Mix grapes into a cream or curd cheese, or combine with cream cheese and ginger.

Place on green salad, or mould the cream or curd cheese into shape and stick small grapes all over the cheese, then serve on lettuce surrounded by grated carrot, with a dressing as Recipe 3.

(29) *Stuffed Green, Red or Yellow Peppers*

Wash peppers, cut off tops and remove seeds.

Mix cream cheese (the amount will depend on size of pepper) with finely chopped parsley and chives to taste, and a few grated nuts if liked, or chopped olives. Stuff into pepper and chill for an hour or so. Just before serving cut with a very sharp knife into thin slices and serve on a bed of lettuce and grated carrot.

(30) *Tomato Salad*

Wash and slice firm tomatoes and place in layers in a bowl. Between each layer sprinkle a little sweet basil, and let them stand for an hour or so. Prepare a bed of lettuce, decorate with grated raw turnips mixed with currants and place a heap of tomato slices in the middle.

(31) *Soaked Germinated Wheat*

Place wheat in bowl, and cover with water. Change water daily until wheat starts to germinate. Can be added to muesli or to winter salads.

(32) *Pear Salad (A)*

Make nest of lettuce leaves, place on this 3 halves of pears with cores removed. Fill the core holes with grated cheese. Decorate with watercress or mustard and cress.

(33) *Pear Winter Salad (A)*

As No. 32, but use raw finely sliced or coarsely grated whiteheart cabbage or savoy instead of lettuce.

(34) *Pear and Carrot Salad (A)*

2 teacups finely grated raw carrot. Make a nest of this on plate, and arrange pear halves filled with grated cheese. Decorate as No. 32.
N.B. — Should fresh pears be scarce or expensive, bottled pears can be used so long as they are bottled in water only — no chemicals used.

(35) *Pineapple Salad (A)*

Arrange lettuce leaves on plate. On top, place 4 rings of fresh pineapple ½ to ¾ inch thick, with centres removed. Chop the latter and stir into grated cheese, allowing 1 tablespoon to each slice of pineapple. Pile mixture into centres of pineapple, and serve.

(36) *Purple Sprouting Broccoli Salad*

Arrange the purple sprouts round plate. Make little piles inside these of the following raw vegetables: ½ cup grated artichoke, ½ cup grated carrot, ¼ cup grated turnip and sultanas, ¼ cup grated beetroot. In the centre place a little heap of raw finely chopped leek.

(37) *Watercress Salad*

Arrange watercress on plate. Place on it a tablespoonful or so of raw grated carrot and turnip and a sliced tomato. Decorate with 3 or 4 sprigs of parsley.

Watercress should be the main ingredient.

(38) *Winter Salad – 1*

Finely grate enough brussels sprouts to fill a teacup, and place on a plate. Add a few leaves of chicory, and 1 tablespoonful of each of the following raw grated vegetables: carrot, swede, parsnip. Add also 1 teaspoon raw chopped leek.

Arrange the ingredients attractively, and decorate with watercress, parsley, or mustard and cress.

(39) *Winter Salad – 2*

Cup of coarsely grated or shredded cabbage, whiteheart or savoy; 2 or 3 small lengths of celery, carrot, swede and parsnip, as in No. 38, also tablespoon of grated raw artichoke. Decorate with watercress or parsley.

The inclusion of shredded root and other vegetables is a distinctive and essential feature of ·winter salads in addition to other conventional saladings according to cost and availability. Ingredients such as chopped nuts, chopped dates, raisins, apple, pineapple, orange, etc., may be included according to taste.

PROTEIN DISHES – WITH STARCH

(40) *An Easy Basic Sauce (F)*

6 level tablespoons wholemeal flour (slightly more or less may be needed as flour varies.)
1 pint of milk or stock
1 oz. of butter

Mix flour with enough liquid from the pint to make a very thin batter. Place the remaining liquid in a saucepan and bring to boil. When boiling, pour in the flour mixture slowly, stirring all the time to prevent lumps and burning. When all has been combined, bring

up to boiling-point, still stirring. Remove
from heat, add butter and whatever flavouring
is desired, such as cheese, parsley, etc.

(41) *Cheese Soufflé (F)*

Make ½ pint thick white sauce, using milk. Let the sauce cool but
not get cold. Beat in the yolks of 3 eggs, and then add 4 oz. grated
cheese. Mix well, and finally add the egg whites beaten stiff — fold
these in and place the mixture in a well-greased fireproof dish.
Bake for 20 to 30 minutes in moderate oven or Reg. 6 (403° F.)
until it has risen and set in the middle. Must be eaten at once,
otherwise it sinks and becomes heavy.

(42) *Cauliflower Cheese*

Wash cauliflower well, cook conservatively until done. Drain well
and place in fireproof oven dish. Cover with a cheese sauce, and
add grated cheese on top. Place in oven until brown on top. Serve
with chopped parsley or paprika sprinkled on the top.

(43) *Gruyère Cheese Balls (F)*

Mashed cooked potatoes to form a stiff paste when rolled out. It is
nicer if a little fresh chopped mint is added to the potato, or dried
mint previously soaked in a little hot water can be used. Remove
the silver paper from the processed Gruyère section or cut Gruyère
cheese into rounds.

Cover cheese sections with potato pastry, roll into balls, dip in
egg and breadcrumbs and fry in *deep-fat* fryer for 5 minutes. Then
turn and fry other side for similar time.

Keep warm in oven until required. They should be brown and
crisp on the outside, and when cut the cheese runs out in a creamy
stream.

The recipe can be varied by cutting the triangles of cheese in half and dipping in egg and breadcrumbs at least twice before frying.

(44) *Egg Nests*

Allow a good tablespoon brown, unpolished rice per person. Cook rice till tender. Drain and rinse to separate the grains. Make a thick white sauce (about ½ pint for 4 servings), add a cup of grated cheese and a little paprika, and stir until cheese has melted. Make individual nests with the rice, which has been kept warm. Place a poached egg in centre, and cover with the cheese sauce. Sprinkle chopped parsley on top.

(45) *Eggs in Potato Cases*

Allow 1 large potato and 1 egg per person.

Well scrub and bake required number of potatoes. When cooked (this depends on size – usually 1½ hours, longer if very large), remove potatoes from oven, cut a thin slice from top, hollow out a cavity large enough to take an egg. Pour in the egg, and return to the oven for the egg to set (about 10 to 15 minutes in a medium oven).

(46) *Haricot Bean Cutlets (F)*

Soak 1 lb. beans overnight. Boil until soft, strain and mash. Add 2 beaten eggs (only 1 if eggs are scarce), mixed herbs if desired, and a cup of grated cheese. Mix well. Shape into cutlets, breadcrumb them and deep fry for 5 minutes on both sides.

If liked, add a little finely chopped onion, which should be fried beforehand.

(47) *Haricot Bean Stew with Dumplings (F)*

Soak ½ lb. haricot beans overnight. Slice and chop 2 onions and fry until brown in a little margarine, then add to a quart of vegetable stock. Add haricot beans. Cut 3 scrubbed carrots into rings 1 inch thick, quarter a scrubbed parsnip and cut into lengths 1 inch long.

Simmer until beans are cooked. Time varies — some beans take longer than others. Add *Vecon* to taste, and thicken either by adding a teaspoon of agar-agar mixed with a little cold water to a paste or some flour. Dumplings can be added during the last ½ hour. These are made with ½ lb. wholemeal self-raising flour, into which a piece of margarine, or vegetable cooking fat (about 1 oz.), has been well rubbed. Moisten with cold water or vegetable stock into a dough, shape into balls, and drop into the stew and continue to simmer. Add grated cheese to taste.

(48) *Roast Lentil Savoury*

Wash and boil 1 lb. lentils until soft. Mash and combine with 1 large chopped onion and 2 cups mashed potatoes, mixed herbs to taste. If too moist, add wholemeal breadcrumbs until the mixture can be formed into a roll.

Place in a greased tin and bake for half an hour or until nicely browned.

(49) *Leek, Cheese and Rolled Oats Pie*

Allow 2 leeks and 1 carrot per person.

Thoroughly clean leeks and carrots. Cut leeks into 1-inch lengths and slice the carrots thinly. Cook conservatively until soft. Grease a pie dish, and place alternate layers of rolled oats, vegetables and grated cheese in this order until the dish is full, ending with a layer of rolled oats and cheese. Pour in the remains of the vegetable water to moisten the rolled oats, which should be moist but not wet or dry when the pie is cooked.

Place in a hot oven for half an hour until the top is nicely browned. Sprinkle with parsley and serve hot.

(50) Macaroni Cheese (F)

Boil ½ lb. of wholemeal macaroni until cooked, usually about ½ hour. Make a white sauce, add 2 oz. grated cheese, and stir until the cheese has melted. Mix in the macaroni and put into a greased oven dish. Sprinkle a little extra grated cheese over, and either place in oven until brown on top, or under grill.

Before serving, sprinkle with chopped parsley or paprika.

(51) Macaroni Vegetable Cheese

Cook a selection of different vegetables (as in season) — e.g. peas, beans, carrots, parsnips, etc. — with 100 per cent wholemeal macaroni. When cooked add a little milk. When boiling, thicken with wholemeal flour mixed to a paste with milk, then add grated cheese to taste. Do not boil after adding cheese. Serve in hot dish or add a little more grated cheese to top and grill until brown.

(52) Vegetables in Cheese Batter (F)

4 oz. 81 per cent plain flour
4 oz. curd cheese
¼ pint milk and water
2 eggs

Combine flour, eggs, milk and water and beat well, then add curd cheese, mix well and beat until smooth. This batter is used to coat conservatively cooked cauliflower florets, sprouts, carrot rings or young whole carrots or 1-inch pieces of salsify.

Coat with batter, then drop into hot deep fat and cook until golden brown. Drain and serve.

(53) *Nutmeat and Egg Pie (F)*

1 tin nutmeat
2 or 3 hard boiled eggs
Peas, cooked — or tin-
   ned peas
1 cooked carrot, diced
Agar-agar mixed with
   vegetable stock
   flavoured with a
   yeast extract
Wholemeal pastry

Line a well-greased oblong bread tin with pastry on bottom and sides. Cut the nutmeat into fair-sized pieces. Fill the pastry case with the nutmeat, peas, carrots, eggs, to the top. Make about a pint of agar-agar. This should have been done previously, as the liquid has to cool. Place the agar-agar, when cool, over the nutmeat and vegetables, and fill to the top.

Place a pastry crust over the top, and bake in a hot oven until the pastry is cooked.

This is served cold with salads.

The ingredients can be varied to taste.

(54) *Baked Nutmeat Potatoes (F)*

Make nutmeat as rissole mixture (No. 78). Scrub 1 large potato per person. Slice off top, scoop out some of the centre, and fill with the nutmeat.

Place in baking tin with a little fat. Cook in medium oven for 1½ to 2 hours. Baste occasionally with the fat.

(55) *Onion Flan (F)*

Make a short pastry, and line a shallow ovenproof dish (Recipe 188).

Slice 2 onions, fairly large ones, parboil, and place on the pastry when cool. Beat 3 eggs into a pint of milk, and pour over the onions. (If only a small dish is being used, ½ pint milk and 2 eggs will suffice.) Chopped parsley can be added to the egg and milk, and also sprinkled on top before being served.

Bake Reg. 6 (403° F.) for 35 to 40 minutes, or until the egg and milk has set.

(56) Cheese and Onion Tart (F)

3 large onions
4 oz. grated cheese
2 oz. butter or oil
3 eggs
Good tablespoon
    flour
½ pint vegetable
    stock or milk
½ teaspoon curry
    powder
Wholemeal or 81 per
    cent pastry (See
    Recipe No. 188)

Chop onions and cook in fat until soft but not browned. Mix flour and curry powder with some of the stock or milk to thin paste. Place remainder in saucepan with onions and bring to boil. Add the thin flour paste and stir until cooked, then remove from heat and stir in cheese until melted. Meanwhile, make pastry and line two flan tins — about 7 or 8-inches across and 1-inch deep — or a large flat casserole top. Add beaten eggs to the now cooled onion mixture and pour into the pastry-lined dish or tins. Bake in oven 350° F. or Reg. 3 until set and brown on top.

(57) Onion and Potato Pie

Well scrub potatoes and slice thinly. Prepare onions and slice. Grease a pie dish. Place alternate layers of sliced potatoes and onions,* a sprinkling of paprika, then potatoes and onions until the dish is full, ending with a layer of potato. Over the top place a layer of grated cheese.

Bake Reg. 6 (403° F.) for ½ hour, remove, and add 2 tablespoons of vegetable stock. Return to oven and bake for another ½ hour, or until done.

* Protein content can be increased in this recipe by adding grated cheese between the layers.

(58) Parsnips au Gratin

Boil required number of parsnips until cooked. Drain well, and place in pie dish. Cover with a cheese sauce, and add grated cheese on top. Place in hot oven or under grill until brown. Serve with chopped parsley or paprika.

Any root vegetables can be served in this way.

(59) *Savoury Cheese Balls (F)*

2 oz. fresh wholemeal
   breadcrumbs
8 oz. grated cheddar
   cheese
2 tablespoons chopped
   parsley
1 teaspoon ground
   nutmeg
2 large beaten eggs

Combine breadcrumbs, parsley, nutmeg and eggs, add cheese, a little milk if not moist enough to roll into balls, dip in flour, then milk, and deep-fat fry until golden.

    4 portions.

(60) *Groundnut Stew*

1 pint water
1 small jar peanut
   butter
1 large chopped onion
Chopped fresh large
   tomato or good
   teaspoon tomato
   purée
1 teaspoon *Barmene*
Hard-boiled eggs and
   brown rice

Chop onion small and cook in ½ pt. of the water with *Barmene* and chopped tomato or tomato purée. Mix peanut butter with the remaining ½ pt. hot water, pour onto the cooking onions and tomato, and boil until it thickens a little.

    Serve with hard-boiled eggs on boiled rice.

(61) *Savoury Rice*

Allow 2 tablespoons of brown, unpolished rice, 1 teaspoon mixed herbs, 1 grated carrot, and ½ chopped onion per person.

Place ingredients in double boiler, washing rice thoroughly first. Add boiling vegetable stock, flavoured with *Vecon*, to cover. As the rice cooks and swells, continue to add the vegetable stock, being careful not to add too much at the end. Cook for half an hour. At the end of this time the rice should be soft and separate — not mushy. If too much stock is added the rice and vegetables will be 'swimming' in the gravy rather than having absorbed nearly all the liquid.

Pile in a warm dish, and serve grated cheese separately.

(62) *Stuffed Peppers with Rice*

Remove top of pepper with stem and the seeds.

Prepare a small amount of savoury rice (No. 61), but use only enough liquid to swell rice. When cooked, fill peppers, and place in a greased baking dish. Cook in moderate oven until brown – about ½ hour. Serve with grated cheese sprinkled over the top.

(63) *Stuffed Spanish Onions (F)*

Use only very large onions. Parboil for 10 minutes, strain, and cut in half. Remove and chop centres. Make a little very thick white sauce, add grated breadcrumbs and cheese to taste, a few chopped nuts, chopped parsley or mixed herbs and the onion centres. Mix well, and pile on to the onion halves. Sprinkle grated cheese on top. Place in baking tin which has had fat melted in it, and bake in a hot oven for an hour.

Breadcrumbs can be omitted, if desired.

(64) *Shepherd's Pie*

3 oz. milled nuts
2 oz. wholemeal breadcrumbs
1 tablespoon soya flour
1 dessertspoon mixed herbs
1 onion, chopped small
1 cup finely grated carrot

Mix all ingredients to a fairly moist consistency with vegetable stock flavoured with *Barmene* or *Vecon*.

Place in greased pie dish, mash cooked potatoes, with skins, with a little milk, margarine and a teaspoon of paprika to a creamy consistency. Place on top of nutmeat, and criss-cross with fork to make ornamental markings.

Cook in hot oven for an hour. Serve with chopped parsley sprinkled over the top.

(If required to be 'fat free,' omit margarine.)

(65) *Cheese Batter with Onions (F)*

Make a Yorkshire pudding batter and let it stand for an hour.

Put plenty of oil in a baking tin and well cover the bottom of the tin with slices of onion. Place in a medium oven until onions are half-cooked and then beat the Yorkshire pudding batter, add grated cheese to taste, pour over the onions and return to oven. Cook at Regulo 7 or 400° F. for from 30 to 40 minutes.

(66) *Soya Bean Savoury (F)*

2 cups cooked soya
  beans
4 slightly heaped
  tablespoons whole-
  meal flour
1 large onion, chopped
  and cooked in
  tablespoon of corn
  oil and 2 tablespoons
  water
1 large teaspoon of
  Barmene or *Vecon*
1½ teaspoons mixed
  sweet herbs
1 egg, well beaten
1 tablespoon *Soya
  Sauce*

Purée the soya beans. Mix *Barmene* or *Vecon* with liquid from cooked onions. Combine all ingredients and mix well, if necessary adding a little water until the mixture can be shaped. Place into an oiled *Pyrex* or fireproof dish and cook in medium oven for 1 hour.

4 portions.

(67) *Stuffed Pine-Kernel Roast (F)*

(With acknowledgements to Janet Walker, author of *Vegetarian Cookery*.)

A special roast for Christmas Day meal or any celebration.

½lb. milled pine kernels
  (saving 1 tablespoon
  whole for decorating
  roast)
½lb. wholemeal bread

Gently fry onion in butter, blend in with beaten eggs, carrot, crumbs and milled nuts with onion, herbs and seasoning and, if necessary, a little hot milk to help bind. Press

crumbs, fresh
2 eggs
2 oz. butter
½lb. grated carrot
1 tablespoon finely
    shredded onion
1 tablespoon fresh and
    finely chopped
    herbs or
1 teaspoon dried herbs
Seasoning if desired
Stuffing:
4 oz. breadcrumbs
2 oz. nut suet
Egg to bind
1 tablespoon finely
    chopped parsley
1 teaspoon thyme and
    sage

out on a floured sheet of kitchen paper then make stuffing.

Mix all together and spread on roast. Roll up with the aid of paper and pat firm. Heat 2 oz. nut suet in baking dish, roll roast in this to coat well, then press on or stick with pine kernels along top to decorate.

Roast in remaining fat in dish at 400° F. or Regulo 5 for about an hour until a good and appetizing golden brown.

When cooked, blend a little flour and some apple or tomato juice in roasting dish and heat to boiling.

Pineapples slices warmed through in the oven are delicious served with this roast.

PROTEIN DISHES — STARCH REDUCED

(68) *Baked Aubergine*

Slice aubergine thinly, and fry until nearly cooked. Place alternate layers of aubergine and sliced tomato in a greased dish. Beat 1 or 2 eggs, and pour over the vegetables. Grate cheese over the top, and place in a medium oven for ½ hour or until set and cooked. Serve with chopped parsley on top.

(69) *Stuffed Aubergine*

Cut aubergine lengthwise, scoop out small seeds in centre and chop them finely. Make small amount of rissole mixture, add the chopped centre, and pile into the aubergine. Place in greased oven dish, and bake in moderate oven for ¾ to 1 hour, depending on size of aubergine.

(70) *Cauliflower Cheese*

Prepare cauliflower as in No. 42, but use the starchless agar-agar sauce (No. 207) with cheese. Otherwise the recipe is the same as No. 42.

(71) *Stuffed Cucumber*

Wash skin, cut lengthwise, remove and chop pips. Make up a rissole mixture, and add chopped centre of cucumber. Pile into cucumber shells and bake for ¾ to 1 hour in medium oven.

(72) *Stuffed Hard-Boiled Eggs*

Cut the hard-boiled eggs into halves, remove the yolks, place in basin and mix yolks with any of the following: chopped nuts and grated cheese, thinly sliced green and red peppers and grated cheese, grated cheese and chopped chives or onions, chopped cooked asparagus tips, chopped cooked or raw mushrooms, chopped celery or chopped purple sprouting broccoli, chopped parsley, marjoram, basil or sage.

Mix the ingredients chosen, and pile into the egg-whites. Paprika can be sprinkled on the stuffed eggs.

(73) *Eggs on Spinach*

Cook spinach, strain and sieve. Place in greased individual fireproof dishes, make a hole in centre and drop in an egg. Place in oven until the egg is cooked. Sprinkle paprika on top, if desired.

(74) *Eggs on Beetroot Tops*

Prepare the beetroot tops as spinach, cook, strain, sieve or chop — then follow No. 73.

(75) *Individual Baked Eggs*

Grease individual dishes. Break the eggs and pour into the dishes. Bake in moderate oven until set — usually about 10 minutes.

(76) *Savoury Fluffy Omelet (F)*

Separate whites and yolks of two eggs. Beat whites very stiff. Beat egg-yolks in another basin for 5 minutes, then add 2 tablespoons hot water and beat again. Have the fat warm in the omelet pan, add parsley or sage chopped finely to the yolk mixture, finally fold in the stiff whites and pour into pan. Cook slowly until done, fold in half, and serve at once. If liked, grated cheese can be placed over the finished omelet, and chopped spring onions or parsley or paprika.

Any cooked chopped vegetable can be used as a filling on top of this omelet before folding.

1 portion.

(77) *Mushroom Savoury (F)*

3 medium mushrooms
2 small leeks or chopped chives
1 large finely grated carrot
5 heaped tablespoons prepared dry nut-meat
½ cup milled nuts
1 teaspoon *Barmene* dissolved in a little vegetable stock or water
Enough vegetable stock to mix all to a stiff paste

Mix nutmeat, milled nuts and grated carrot with dissolved *Barmene* in stock to make a paste. Well grease three individual Pyrex or fireproof dishes, and place a layer of nutmeat on the bottom. Place a mushroom in centre of each, and surround it with chopped leek or chives (onions are rather strong and kill the delicate flavour of the mushrooms). Divide the remaining nutmeat into three portions, make into rounds, flatten or roll them out, and cover the mushroom and chopped leek with the nutmeat 'pastry.' Place dabs of margarine on top, and bake in a medium oven for 1 hour. 3 portions.

(78) *Nut Savoury — 1*

(For baking, or as a stuffing, or for rissoles (F).)

½ packet *Nutmeat Mixture* (Health Food Stores)
1 cup finely grated raw carrot
1 onion sliced and chopped
1 cup grated cheese
1 tablespoon soya flour

Dissolve a large teaspoon of yeast extract in vegetable stock — enough to moisten all the ingredients, which should be well mixed to form a firm paste. Use as stuffing, or bake in oven, or shape into rissoles, dip in beaten egg, roll in milled nuts or breadcrumbs and deep-fat fry for 5 minutes on each side.

4 large portions or 6 small.

(79) *Nut Savoury — 2*

½ packet *Nutmeat Mixture*
1 cup milled nuts
1 dessertspoon mixed herbs
1 teaspoon *Barmene* dissolved in a little vegetable stock or water
Chopped onion to taste
½ cup finely grated parsnip
½ cup finely grated carrot
2 eggs well beaten
1 tablespoon soya flour

This is a variation of Recipe 78 and can be used in the same ways.

4 large portions or 6 small.

(80) *Stuffed Onions*

Prepare as No. 63, but use the starchless agar-agar (No. 207) instead of the basic white sauce.

(81) Stuffed Red, Green or Yellow Peppers (F)

Prepare rissole mixture (No. 78 or 79). Use one pepper per person. Slice off the top with the stem, remove seeds, fill with the nutmeat, and place in a greased baking dish. Bake in a moderate oven until nicely brown. If liked, rissole mixture can be baked before stuffing the peppers.

With the uncooked mixture time in oven varies from ½ to ¾ hour. Baste regularly.

(82) Shepherd's Pie (F)

Prepare as in No. 64, but omit potatoes on top. Instead, use cooked mashed swede, turnip, or swede and turnip combined. Mash with fork and add a little margarine in dabs, and bake Reg. 7 (424° F.) for an hour.

(83) Spinach Beet Cheese

Well wash and cook spinach beet. Add no water, turn frequently to stop burning. Strain and chop or sieve. Add grated cheese to taste. Place in greased fireproof dish, cover with grated cheese and bake Reg. 7 or 8 (424°-446° F.) until brown on top — or, if preferred, after it has warmed through, place under grill to brown.

(84) Soya Flour Noodles

½ lb. soya flour
1 beaten egg
Cold water

Mix egg into soya flour with enough cold water to make a thick paste. Let it stand for a little while and then roll out thinly and fold into a long roll. Cut into thin slices and drop into a large saucepan of boiling water for five minutes, then drain and serve with cheese sauce, parsley sauce or by itself.

(85) *Baked Soya Beans*
(With acknowledgements to Mrs Beatrice Wood.)

2 cups boiled soya
   beans
1 cup strained tomato
   pulp
1 tablespoon brown
   flour
1 tablespoon chopped
   parsley
1 tablespoon chopped
   onion
Seasoning

Make a tomato sauce by mixing the flour and vegetables with the tomato pulp and heating it until it thickens. Pour over the beans and bake until brown in a moderate oven.

    4 portions.

(86) *Scotch Eggs*

4 hard-boiled eggs
Slightly more than ½
   packet of vegetarian
   nut rissole mixture
   (77 or 78)
Barmene or *Vecon*

Dissolve *Barmene* or *Vecon* to taste and mix it with the nut rissole mixture with enough boiling water to make a firm, smooth paste. Mould the paste round each egg to cover completely. Dip in egg and breadcrumbs and fry each side until golden. Serve hot or cold.

(87) *Cashew Nut Savoury*

½ lb. whole cashew
   nuts
¼ lb. mushrooms
1 large onion
1 or 2 carrots
Vegetarian soup powder

Wash nuts in cold water, then stew together with chopped onion and grated carrots. Add washed and coarsely broken up mushrooms when nuts are nearly cooked. Make gravy with the soup powder plus liquid from stewed nuts, then mix gravy with nuts and vegetables, and add any herb or other seasoning that may be desired.

    Serve the stew direct from pan or put it to bake in oven for a short while in heat-proof dish.

(88) Buck-wheat Rissoles (F)

1 cup Buck-wheat
2 cups water
1 large onion (chopped)
1 good tablespoon 100
  per cent wholemeal
  flour
2-3 ozs. grated cheese

Add water to buck-wheat and boil for 2 minutes, then cover and stand for 20 minutes.

Sauté onions in a little oil until cooked but not browned, mix in flour and cook gently, then add buck-wheat. If too dry add a little vegetable stock. Mix in cheese, form into six rissoles, coat with egg and breadcrumbs and deep-fat fry or bake in oven.

PROTOVEG

Protoveg is in our opinion one of the nicer textured protein foods on the market at the moment. It is made by Direct Foods Ltd., which is licensed for the benefit of *Compassion in World Farming* (a Public Trust). All profits will be recycled for further development of protein direct from the growing crop.

There is an unflavoured pack and various specific flavours — all of which are of 100 per cent vegetarian origin.

To hydrate Protoveg

Simply add water or vegetable stock and simmer-
    for chunky - 20 minutes
    for mince — 2 minutes
Normally, two cups of liquid is sufficient for one cup of *Protoveg*.

(89) Hotpot

5 oz. *Protoveg* chunks
3 carrots
1 large onion
1 lb. potatoes
1 pt. vegetable stock
Barmene to taste

Hydrate chunks, layer a casserole dish with thin slices of potato, then place sliced onion, carrots and *Protoveg* in layers, finishing with sliced potatoes.

Add liquid, cover with lid and cook in oven 325° F. or Regulo 3 for two hours.

(90) *Moussaka (F)*

1 lb. hydrated *Protoveg* mince
1 large onion and 2 garlic cloves
1 small tin tomato puree
1 large aubergine
1 egg-yolk
1 teaspoon *Barmene*
3 tablespoons fresh cream
6 oz. grated cheddar cheese
Oil
Bay leaf

Sauté chopped onion and garlic in oil until soft, then remove from the pan. Brown the sliced aubergine in the remaining oil, add mince, tomato purée and bay leaf to ¼ pt. vegetable stock in saucepan, and simmer about 10 minutes. Place alternate layers of aubergine, mince, onion and cheese in a casserole, saving 2 oz. of the cheese. Bake at 350° F. or Regulo 4 for 45 minutes. Mix egg-yolk with cream, pour over the top and sprinkle with remaining cheese. Return to oven for 5 minutes.

(91) *Stew*

1 cup chunky *Protoveg*
3 cups water
1 sliced medium onion
2 large carrots
2 teaspoons tomato purée
Bay leaf
Barmene
Other vegetables as available

Slightly sauté onion in oil. Simmer *Protoveg* in the 3 cups of water with bay leaf and *Barmene*. Add diced vegetables and simmer for 20 minutes or until vegetables are tender. Remove bay leaf, and thicken with a little 100 per cent flour if desired.

N.B. *Protoveg* can be used in many and varied recipes — e.g., rissoles, shepherd's pie, pasties, curries, etc.

COOKED VEGETABLE DISHES

Conservative Cooking

Conservative cooking should be done as follows:

About 1 or 2 cups of water (quantity of water depends on size of saucepan and amount of vegetables) are brought to boil, and the vegetables, cut or shredded (*e.g.* carrots, etc., cut in rounds or quarters, cabbage shredded, sprouts whole), are added. Place lid on tightly, shake frequently to prevent burning, and add a little more water if necessary. All root vegetables can be cooked together. Root vegetables take from 10 to 20 minutes if young and small, longer if old. Green vegetables take from 10 to 20 minutes according to size and age. No salt or soda to be used.

Recipes with white sauce are marked (F). If required to be 'fat free,' omit white sauce.

(92) *Aubergines (F)*

Cut into rings, place in frying pan or saucepan in which a little margarine has been melted, and cook until soft, shaking and moving so that the rings do not burn. When cooked, place in hot dish and keep warm. Make a very little white sauce, and when cooked add at least 2 tablespoons chopped parsley to make it a rich green colour. Pour over aubergines and serve. Alternatively, the aubergines can be cooked in a casserole until done and the sauce then poured over them.

(93) *Aubergine Fritters (F)*

Slice aubergine lengthways or in rings, dip into batter, and fry in deep fat to a golden colour. Drain and serve immediately.

(94) *Aubergine and Onion Casserole*

Well grease casserole, place in it alternate layers of sliced aubergine and onion. Top with a layer of tomato if liked. Cover and place in moderate oven for 1 hour or until cooked.

(95) *Whole Broad Beans (F)*

For this recipe the beans must be young. Well wash the bean pods, do not remove the beans, *the whole vegetable is used*. Cut into lengths of 1½ inches. Cook conservatively for 10 to 15 minutes. While beans are cooking make a white sauce, and at the last minute add 2 to 3 tablespoons chopped parsley. When beans are cooked, drain well and cover with sauce. Sprinkle more chopped parsley on top.

(96) *French Beans*

Top and tail. Cook conservatively for 15 to 20 minutes, according to age. Can be served with a few mushrooms sliced and browned in fat — or grilled — arranged on top of beans; or make a little white sauce, add chopped spring onions and pour over the cooked beans. This recipe is (F) if mushrooms are included.

(97) *Runner or French Bean and Red Pimento Casserole (F)*

Cook beans conservatively. Remove seeds from 1 or 2 pimentos, then slice and chop. Make a little white sauce, add enough grated cheese to flavour. Combine the sauce and vegetables. Grease a fireproof dish, pour the vegetables in, and bake in a moderate oven for 20 minutes. Decorate with parsley.

(98) *Broccoli or Cauliflower Flowerets (F)*

Thoroughly wash, break into little flowerets, parboil 10 minutes, drain, dip into egg and then into breadcrumbs, fine oatmeal or batter. Deep-fry until a golden brown. Serve with parsley sprigs.

(99) *Broccoli or Cauliflower with Parsley Sauce (F)*

Wash well. If large, quarter and place stem down in saucepan in which there is a little boiling water. Place lid on firmly, and cook for 15 to 20 minutes. During this time make a white sauce, pouring consistency; wash and at last minute chop and add parsley (enough to colour sauce really green). By this time cauliflower should be cooked. Strain well, and pour over sauce. Sprinkle paprika on top, if liked, and serve.

(100) *Brussels Sprouts*

Clean, remove dead or damaged leaves, cut a cross in stalks. Place in a little boiling water, put on lid, boil for 10 to 15 minutes, according to size.

(101) *Brussels Sprouts and Chestnuts (F)*

Split the skin on the chestnuts with a sharp knife, making the cuts like a cross. Boil for 10 minutes. Do not strain the water away, as it is easier to remove the skins while the nut is hot. Remove skins.

Prepare the sprouts and cook as in No. 100, only place the chestnuts on top. While cooking, prepare a white sauce and add lots of chopped parsley. Strain sprouts and chestnuts when cooked. Pour over the sauce and serve at once.

(102) *Brussels Sprouts and Chestnut Purée (F)*

Prepare sprouts and chestnuts as in Recipe 101. When cooked mash together well, adding a lump of butter or soft vegetarian margarine when mashing, make into a mound and serve as it is or topped with a little parsley sauce.

Many shops these days sell a plain chestnut purée — not the sweetened variety — which is most useful for this recipe if whole chestnuts are not available.

(103) *Brussels Sprouts Surprise (F)*

Cook sprouts conservatively. Drain well, dip in beaten egg and then in breadcrumbs. Deep-fry until brown. Drain and place in warm dish. Sprinkle with a very little grated cheese and paprika.

(104) *Brussels Sprouts with Celery (F)*

Clean sprouts and celery. Chop celery into 1-inch lengths. Cook sprouts and celery together conservatively for about 15 minutes, and drain. Only a little liquor should be left at the end of cooking, to which add a knob of margarine and thicken with a little wholemeal flour. If desired, ½ teaspoon of *Vecon* can be added to give more flavour. Place vegetables in warm dish. Pour the sauce over, and top with a little milled nuts.

(105) *Boiled Beetroot (F)*

Scrub well. Cut into 1-inch squares or rounds. Place in boiling water, and cook until done. Time depends on age usually and size — 30 to 40 minutes should suffice. If very young, less time is necessary. Drain well. Make a sauce, using the beetroot water thickened with wholemeal flour and margarine in the usual way for a white sauce. Add paprika to flavour.

At the last minute add plenty of chopped parsley, and pour over the hot beet. Serve with extra parsley on top. If liked, omit parsley and add grated orange peel.

(106) *Roast Beetroot (F)*

Scrub well. If medium size, cut in half; if large, cut in quarters. Place in hot fat in baking tin or fireproof dish and roast for 1¼ hours, or until done, in moderate oven. All root vegetables, except swedes, can be cooked like this. Swedes should be boiled first until almost cooked, and can then be finished off in a like manner.

(107) *Young Beetroot Tops*

Well wash the beetroot leaves. Remove any really tough stalks. Boil conservatively for 15 to 20 minutes. Strain, chop or sieve if liked, and serve.

This is a very pleasant vegetable.

(108) *White or Purple Sprouting Broccoli*

Wash well. Remove any stringy pieces. Boil a little water, and place the green leaves in first, piling the sprouts on top. They should be cooked in about 15 minutes. When done, remove sprouts carefully to keep them whole, and drain well. Strain the green leaves, and place in a warm dish with sprouts on top. Serve at once.

Cauliflower
   See Nos. 98 and 99.

(109) *Carrot Tops*

Use young carrot tops. Remove the long stems, and, after washing, cook conservatively for 20 to 25 minutes. Strain, chop, and serve hot.

(110) *Boiled Carrots*

Scrub well. Remove any damaged parts and top. If young, leave whole and cook conservatively for 20 minutes (less if very small). Strain and serve. If the carrots are old, slice into thin rings and cook for 15 to 20 minutes.

(111) *Carrots and Peas*

Cut carrots into rings, shuck peas. Place the two vegetables into a very little boiling water, carrots first, peas on top, and cook for 15 to 20 minutes. Serve in warm dish.

(112) *Braised Carrots*

Scrub carrots well. Cut into quarters lengthways. Place in well-greased casserole, add 2 tablespoons vegetable stock, cover and cook in moderate oven for 1 hour. Peas can be added after ½ hour as they cook in shorter time.

(113) *Creamed Cabbage (F)*

Wash well, then chop or shred coarsely. Boil conservatively 15 to 20 minutes, strain. Fry 1 onion, chopped, in margarine. Add flour and vegetable stock to make a thick brown sauce. Mix in ½ teaspoon of *Vecon* to flavour. Place sauce and cabbage in saucepan, and stir well while it warms through. Serve when hot.

(114) *Celeriac (F)*

Scrub well. If old, remove fibrous outside. Cut into squares or rounds ½ to ¾ inch in size. Place in cold water and bring to boil. Time will vary according to age or size — usually ½ to ¾ hour will suffice. Drain well, and serve with a white sauce flavoured with a little cheese or chopped parsley.

(115) *Celeriac Casserole*

Prepare as No. 114. Place in a little water, boil for a few minutes, and drain. Have a well-greased casserole ready, and place layers of celeriac and onion alternately with a little chopped parsley and thyme every so often.

Add a little vegetable stock to cover the bottom of the casserole, and place in a moderate oven until celeriac is cooked (about 1 to 1½ hours).

(116) *Braised Celery (F)*

Select fairly small celery heads and wash well. Cut into halves lengthwise, place in a long casserole and add a little vegetable stock. Cook in moderate oven until done (usually 1½ to 1¾ hours). Make a brown sauce with vegetable stock, thicken and then flavour with *Vecon*. Pour over celery and serve. If liked, the celery may be cooked in the brown sauce.

(117) *Boiled Celery (F)*

Wash celery thoroughly, chop into 2-inch lengths, and place in boiling water. Cook for 20 to 30 minutes, less if young and tender. Strain well, and serve with a sauce flavoured with cheese, parsley, or mixed herbs.

(118) *Chestnut Roast (F)*

1 lb. mashed chestnuts
Grated rind of 1 large lemon
1 oz. butter (melted)
1 teaspoon soft brown sugar
4 oz. fresh wholemeal breadcrumbs
2 tablespoons chopped parsley
1 large egg

Combine all ingredients well so that the mixture is firm enough to mould into a round or long shape. If too dry, add a little vegetable stock until it can be moulded; if not dry enough add a few more breadcrumbs. Place on greased oven-proof dish or plate, cover with foil and cook for about 1 hour at 400° F. or Regulo 5.   4 to 5 portions.

(119) *Salsify (or Oyster Plant) with Parsley Sauce*

Scrub or scrape salsify, cut into 1-inch lengths and drop into boiling water until cooked (anything from 20 to 45 minutes, according to size), then drain and cover with parsley sauce.

Variations: Cover with a cheese sauce, or, when cooked and drained, roll in flour and deep fry.

(120) *Chestnut and Celery Casserole (F)*

Skin chestnuts as in No. 101. Wash celery well, and cut into 2-inch lengths. Place chestnuts and celery in casserole. Make a thick brown sauce with vegetable stock. It can be thickened with flour and margarine and *Vecon* added, or a vegetarian brown soup powder can be used. Grate a nutmeg, and add to sauce and pour over the vegetables. Nutmeg can be omitted, but it definitely adds to this dish.

Pour sauce over celery and chestnuts, and cover. Cook in moderate oven for 2 hours. For the last ½ hour remove top so that sauce thickens.

(121) *Chestnut and Onion Casserole (F)*

Prepare as No. 120, but use onion instead of celery.

(122) Chicory (F)

Wash, cut in half lengthwise. Place in well-greased casserole with a little vegetable stock, and cook in moderate oven until done (¾ to 1 hour).

Serve with dabs of margarine, parsley sauce, or a cheese sauce.

(123) Corn on the Cob (F)

Young corn should be a pale creamy yellow, not deep yellow. Remove husks and silk, and drop into boiling water for 10 minutes. Sometimes 15 minutes is required if corn is getting old. Drain well, and serve with butter.

(124) Boiled Cucumber (F)

Wash skin. Cut lengthwise and then into 2-inch lengths or 1-inch rounds if preferred. Boil until tender (about 20 to 30 minutes, sometimes less if young). Drain and serve with a parsley sauce, paprika sauce, or cheese sauce.

(125) Roast Cucumber (F)

Wash skin, cut down centre. Place in hot fat in fireproof dish and roast until done (about ¾ hour) in moderate oven.

(126) Fried Cucumber (F)

Cut into circles about ½ to ¾ inch thick. Dip in flour seasoned with paprika and mixed herbs, and fry in deep fat to a golden brown (about 5 minutes each side).

(127) Kohl Rabi (F)

This can be used as two vegetables. The green leaves can be well washed and conservatively cooked for about 15 minutes, strained and served.

The bulbous part can be well washed and scrubbed. If old, remove the fibrous outside skin, boil conservatively for 20 to 25 minutes, strain, and serve with parsley or cheese sauce.

(128) *Kale*

Remove all thick tough stems, wash well, and cook conservatively for 20 to 25 minutes. Strain and serve.

(129) *Boiled Leeks (F)*

Remove old or bruised leaves — the young green tips can also be used. Slit down centre, and wash well in tepid water to remove earth from between leaves. Place in boiling water and cook for 20 to 25 minutes. Strain and serve with parsley, paprika, or cheese sauce.

(130) *Braised Leeks*

Wash leeks well as in No. 129. Place in casserole with a little vegetable stock. This can be flavoured with *Vecon* if liked. Cover and cook in moderate oven for about an hour. Sprinkle chopped parsley on top before serving.

(131) *Lettuce and Peas (F)*

Wash lettuce well, and place half the amount in saucepan. Water will run off the leaves into the saucepan, but it is just as well to add 3 or 4 tablespoons of vegetable stock as well. On top of the lettuce place the required amount of young peas. Cover with the remainder of the wet lettuce. Cover and simmer for 20 to 25 minutes, shaking every so often to stop burning. Drain, place in warm dish, dab the top with margarine, and serve.

Mint can also be placed in the middle with the peas, and a little chopped mint can be placed on top before serving.

(132) *Lettuce, Pea and Carrot Casserole (F)*

Wash lettuce well, scrub carrots and shuck peas. Grease casserole well, place layers of lettuce, young peas and young carrots cut into rounds ¼ inch thick alternately until all the vegetables are used. Top with dabs of margarine, and add a tablespoon of vegetable stock. Cover and cook in moderate oven for 1 hour. Serve at once.

Peas can also be steamed with sprigs of mint, or boiled. When young, only a few minutes are required.

(133) *Mushroom Casserole*

Wash, and peel if old. Place in casserole with a very little boiling milk, cover and cook in moderate oven for 20 minutes to ½ hour, according to size and serve. (A few extra stalks can be added if liked.)

(134) *Grilled Mushrooms*

Prepare as above. Place under stove grill, and cook for about 5 minutes. Turn and grill the other side for the same length of time, and serve.

(135) *Mushrooms and Cheese Sauce (F)*

Prepare and cook as in No. 133. Melt a little fat, add flour, and mix well. Add a little cold milk, mix in, and then add the hot milk from casserole. Bring to the boil slowly, stirring all the time. If too thick, add more milk. Add enough grated cheese to flavour. Pour over the mushrooms, return to oven to warm through, and serve.

(136) *Marrow (F)*

If young and small, do not remove seeds. Skin, cut into rounds, and steam or boil conservatively until soft. Strain well. Serve with parsley sauce or onion sauce.

(137) *Roast Marrow (F)*

Do not remove skin and seeds if young. Cut into rounds — or, if old and large, oblong — and place in baking dish with hot fat. Cook for 1½ to 2 hours, turning every so often.

(138) *Spring Onion Casserole*

Remove roots and any damaged green leaves. Wash well. Place in greased casserole, add a tablespoon of vegetable stock, cover, and cook in moderate oven for 30 minutes, or until soft.

(139) *Boiled Spring Onions (F)*

Prepare as in No. 138. Cook conservatively for 10 minutes, drain, and serve with parsley or cheese sauce, or just chopped parsley sprinkled over the top.

(140) *Devilled Parsnips (S, F)*

Scrub well, cut in half lengthwise, and parboil for 10 minutes. Drain well, and place in baking tin, the bottom of which is just covered with hot fat. Sprinkle brown sugar over the parsnips, and cook in moderate oven for 1 hour, or until soft, turning and basting two or three times.

(141) *Boiled Parsnips*

Scrub well and then cut into fingers. Boil a little water (about 1½ cupfuls), add parsnips, cover, and boil for approximately 25 minutes. Drain well and serve. A little melted butter or margarine can be poured over, if liked (F).

(142) *Creamed Parsnips (F)*

Prepare and cook as in No. 141. Drain well, and mash to a cream. Add a little milk and margarine to make it more creamy. If liked, place in fireproof dish, mark with fork, and brown under grill.

(143) *Parsnip Balls (F)*

Prepare as in No. 142. When parsnips are creamed, add a beaten egg and a little flour. Fashion the paste into balls or rissole shapes, and deep-fat fry until golden brown on outside.

(144) *Baked Potatoes*

Use large, even-sized potatoes. Scrub well, remove eyes, wipe over with a greased paper. Slit each side with a sharp knife, and bake in moderate oven for 1 to 1½ hours according to size.

(145) *Stuffed Potatoes (F)*

Prepare and cook as in No. 144, but do not slit sides. When done, remove and allow to cool for a minute. Slice off a thin layer from top. Scoop out potato into a bowl — do not break skin case. Add a little hot milk and butter, mash well to a thick cream, and then combine with one of the following fillings: chopped parsley, mixed herbs, a little grated cheese and pinch of nutmeg, beaten egg, a few caraway seeds.

Mix well, and pile back into the potato cases, mark with fork, return to oven to warm up and brown on the top.

(146) *Roast Potatoes (F)*

Scrub well and remove eyes. Cut in half (or quarters if large), place in baking tin in hot fat and roast in moderate oven 1½ to 2 hours, turning every so often. The time depends on size of potatoes.

(147) *Creamed Peas (F)*

Steam very young peas. When soft, mash to paste and add lump of butter. Serve very hot with chopped mint sprinkled over the top.

(148) *Creamed Peas and Mushrooms (F)*

Prepare peas as in No. 147. Clean mushrooms, leaving whole but removing stalk, and grill as in No. 134. When cooked, fill centres with the creamed peas and serve hot.

(149) *Peppers with Tomatoes (F)*

Remove stems and seeds from the peppers. Slice into lengths. Slice the tomatoes, place both vegetables in a saucepan with a knob of margarine, and cook until tender.

(150) *Radish Tops*

Prepare and cook as in No. 163, but remove the stems first.

(151) *Fried Radishes (F)*

Prepare and clean, slice and fry in hot fat 6 or 7 minutes each side. Move the radishes round in the pan to stop burning. Serve very hot.

(152) *Spinach Beet*

Wash the leaves very well in several changes of water. When clean, place straight in saucepan. Enough water will fall off the washed leaves, so do not add any more. Cover and cook for 10 to 15 minutes, turning occasionally to stop burning. Strain, chop lightly, add a knob of margarine, if liked, return to saucepan, and warm through.

(153) *Spinach Beet or Swiss Chard (F)*

Prepare and cook leaves as in No. 152, having first removed the thick stems. Wash the stems well, cut into 2-inch lengths, and cook conservatively until soft. (Time varies with age of plant.) Strain and cover with a thick parsley sauce, so that this provides two vegetable dishes out of one.

(154) *Creamed Spinach Beet (F)*

Prepare and cook spinach beet as in No. 152 then add the brown onion sauce as in No. 113. Mix well and serve hot.

(155) *Sweet Potatoes, Baked (F)*

Prepare and cook in the same manner as No. 144, but allow longer time in oven. Serve with butter pats.

(156) *Grilled Tomatoes (S)*

Wash and cut in halves, place on griller, cut sides uppermost. Sprinkle with brown sugar, and grill slowly for 15 minutes, or until cooked. Serve with chopped parsley sprinkled on top.

(157) *Baked Tomatoes and Onions (F)*

Wash tomatoes, peel and slice onions. Butter fireproof dish and line with onion slices. Place tomatoes either whole or cut in half on top, and cover with more onion slices. Dot with margarine, and cook in moderate oven until done and brown on top — or cook in a covered casserole.

(158) Stuffed Tomatoes with Mushrooms (F)

Clean and chop mushrooms. Melt a little fat in frying pan, and sauté mushrooms for 2 or 3 minutes, keeping them on the move. Slice the top from the tomatoes, scoop out centres, and chop and mix with the mushrooms; pile back into the tomato cups, and bake in moderate oven for 15 to 20 minutes. Serve with parsley sprinkled on top.

(159) Turnips

These can be prepared and cooked in the same way as carrots in Nos. 110 and 112.

(160) Creamed Turnips (F)

Scrub well and cut into cubes. Drop into a little boiling water, and simmer until tender. Strain and add a knob of margarine and mash. Serve hot.

(161) Boiled Turnips (F)

Scrub well. If small, leave whole. Place in boiling water and simmer until soft, drain, and serve with parsley sauce, or dot with margarine and sprinkle with chopped parsley.

(162) Roast Turnips (F)

Scrub well. Cut into halves or quarters, if large. Place in hot fat in baking dish, and cook in moderate oven for 1 to 1½ hours until soft, turning every so often.

(163) *Turnip Tops*

Wash well, remove hard stems. Cook in very little boiling water 15 to 20 minutes according to age. Strain, chop, and serve hot. Dot with margarine, if desired.

SECOND COURSES

UNCOOKED

All fresh fruit comes under this heading that is not heated, canned or bottled in any way.

Fruit salads can be prepared beforehand and allowed to soak in their own juices.

The following are mainly acid or sub-acid fruits (see table on page 124): strawberries, whole or crushed; raspberries, whole or crushed; grapes; sliced oranges; diced apples; sultanas; diced pears; pineapple cut into rings or cubes; red, white and black currants; peaches; apricots. All can be combined to make up many different fruit salads, or used separately in agar-agar jelly made from water and fruit juices — for example:

(164) *Orange Jelly (A)*

1 pint prepared agar-agar, made from water and juice of an orange (1 large or 2 small oranges).

Prepare agar-agar, grate in orange skin to taste. Remove pith, and chop orange finely. When jelly is cool, mix in orange, and pour into individual dishes.

(165) *Yogurt* can be served with any of the following:
  Molasses
  Black treacle
  Brown pieces sugar
  Fresh raw fruit in season

COOKED, WITH STARCH

The following two sections of second courses may have to be omitted from special diets, as recommended by the practitioner.

The section 'cooked, starch reduced' may be used in some cases by diabetics, provided sugar is omitted or reduced to a minimum according to the severity of the case. In some of these honey may be substituted for sugar as a sweetening agent, as part of the sugar in honey consists of fructose, which is tolerated by diabetics. The diabetic patient should be advised by his practitioner in this matter.

(166) *Treacle Tart (S, F)*

Line greased tin or baking plate with wholemeal pastry (No. 188). Cover the pastry with soft wholemeal breadcrumbs. Add cane syrup or black treacle to cover, and bake in moderate oven until pastry is done.

(167) *Date Crumble (S, F)*

Cut up the dates, and stew until soft in only a little water, so that when done, there is not a lot of liquid left. Place in fireproof dish or individual dishes. Cover with the following:

Equal amounts of fat and wholemeal flour, brown sugar to sweeten if desired. Mix all together as for a pastry mixture, but do not add any liquid.

Place the mixture on top of cooked dates, press down lightly and prick top for decoration. Bake in moderate oven for ½ hour or until top is a nice brown.

Prunes or figs or dried apricots can be used instead of dates.

(168) Bakewell Pudding (S, F)

Wholemeal pastry (as
  recipe 188)
4 oz. ground almonds
  or milled nuts
2 eggs
2 or 3 oz. brown sugar,
  to taste
Jam

Grease a dish or baking plate, line with pastry, and cover with a little jam. Beat eggs, and mix in the nuts and sugar. Place on pastry, and bake 20 to 30 minutes in moderate oven.

(169) Banana and Agar-Agar Junket

Mix 2 level teaspoons agar-agar in a little water, add 1 pint milk and heat to boiling point, while stirring. Pour over sliced banana in bowl or individual dishes, and let cool.

(170) Bread Pudding (S, F)

1 lb. wholemeal bread
2 oz. wholemeal flour
4 oz. brown sugar
3 oz. currants
3 oz. sultanas
3 oz. grated vegetarian
  cooking fat
1 beaten egg
Nutmeg and mixed
  spice to taste
A little milk, or milk
  and water

Soak bread in milk until soft. Squeeze dry, and beat up with other ingredients. Melt some extra fat in a baking dish to cover the bottom, and, when hot, place the mixture in the dish. Sprinkle with a little extra sugar, and return to oven. Bake at moderate heat for 2 hours.

If preferred, can be steamed for 2 hours instead.

(171) Melon Surprise

Slice off top of melon, remove pips, remove melon flesh with small round scoop to make little balls. Stuff lychees (1 small tin) with stoned cherries. Return all to melon skin and chill.

COOKED, STARCH REDUCED

(172) *Agar-Agar Custard*

1 pint fresh milk
2 teaspoons agar-agar
Vanilla or almond essence
Heaped dessertspoon demerara sugar

Mix the agar-agar with ½ cup of cold water until it is without lumps. Then add gradually the pint of cold milk. Bring the mixture to the boil, stirring all the time, and then simmer for a minute. Serve hot.

(173) *Agar-Agar Egg Custard Mould*

Make as Recipe 172 but add two beaten eggs after mixture has cooled a little. Pour into a wetted mould and turn out when cold.

(174) *Caramel Pears (S, A)*

Allow 1 whole pear per person. Peel and cut in half and remove core, or let them remain whole. Simmer in a little water until cooked but not mushy. Remove carefully, drain, and place the whole pear or 2 halves in individual dishes. Make a thick caramel with some of the water that remains by adding a little of it to ½ cup of brown sugar and boiling until dark brown and thick. Coat the pears with it, and serve cold.

(175) *Chocolate Mould*

1 tablespoon agar-agar
2 tablespoons brown sugar
2 tablespoons cocoa
1 pint milk
1 cup water to mix agar-agar

Boil milk, combine cocoa and sugar and mix to a paste with some hot milk, add rest of milk, mix agar-agar with the cold water and add to the hot cocoa mixture. Replace over heat and bring to simmering point, stirring all the time. Simmer for 2 minutes. Turn into mould.

(176) *Stuffed Prunes*

Soak or steam prunes until swollen and fairly soft. Slit down one side and remove stone. Fill with a little grated cheese or cream cheese. Place in sweet papers and arrange on dish. Instead of being served as a sweet, they can be used on a salad.

(177) *Peach or Apricot Islands (S, A)*

Make an agar-agar egg custard mould (No. 173). Halve peaches or apricots, remove stones. Dot over the egg custard when cooked and cold, round side up, or, if using individual dishes, place one half in centre of each dish.

(178) *Marrow Meringue (S, F)*

Peel and remove the marrow seeds. Cut marrow in slices, and cook conservatively until done. Drain well. Mash the marrow, and add brown sugar to taste, add a walnut of margarine, 2 egg-yolks and a little ground cinnamon. Mix well, and place in greased heat-proof dish. Beat egg-whites stiff, and place on top. Bake in a medium oven until the egg-white is a delicate brown.

(179) *Baked Grapefruit (A)*

Cut fruit in half, remove pith or core in centre, and fill with honey. Place the fruit halves in individual heatproof dishes and cook in moderate oven until warmed through and the fruit looks plump on top (usually about 15 minutes). Place a cherry in centre, and serve hot.

(180) *Apple Fool (S, A)*

Prepare apples for stewing, and cook with very little liquid until soft and fluffy. Sieve or beat well, and add thick cream. Sweeten with honey if desired. Place in individual dishes, and serve cold. Desiccated coconut may be sprinkled on top.

(181) *Apple Meringue (S, A)*

Prepare apples, and cook in a little water until very soft. Beat well, sweeten with honey to taste, and place in fireproof dish. Beat up the whites of 2 eggs until stiff, add a little sugar, and pile on top of apple. Cook in oven until brown. Serve hot or cold.

BREAKFAST DISHES

WITH STARCH

(182) *Muesli — 1*

1 tablespoon coarse oatmeal
3 tablespoons water

Leave to soak all night. Next morning, add 1 tablespoon nut cream and grated carrot. Mix well, and serve.

Whole grated apples and skin of lemon grated finely can be added instead of carrot.

(182A) *Muesli — 2*

1 tablespoon coarse oatmeal
3 tablespoons water

Leave to soak all night. Next morning, add the following: chopped stewed figs, dates, or prunes; 1 dessertspoon milled nuts; grated skin of lemon to taste, if liked; 1 dessertspoon honey; 1 dessertspoon nut cream. Mix well and serve.

(183) *Oatmeal Porridge*

8 tablespoons coarse oatmeal
2 pints water

Place in double boiler, and cook for 1 hour. Can be warmed up when required.

Various wholefood breakfast cereals are sold by Health Food Stores.

STARCH REDUCED

(184) *Natural Bran, Wheatgerm and Stewed Dried Fruit (L)*

2 tablespoons bran. 1 tablespoon wheatgerm, stewed or soaked figs, dates, prunes or soaked raisins. Add top of milk if liked.

(185) *Fresh Fruit (A)*

Any fresh fruit in season, except bananas, which are starchy.

BREAD, CAKES, TARTS

A small number of cakes and tarts, etc., have been included in this section. While these are not usually included in a strictly Diet Reform diet, and, in any case, will be omitted from a strict therapeutic diet, they may be included in moderation in the normal person's diet if only to add variety and interest. It will be seen that the recipes are made from whole foods, and a further variety of recipes may be obtained from conventional sources by substituting whole food ingredients for the usual over-refined, processed ingredients. Whole foods, as mentioned elsewhere, may be obtained from Health Food Stores.

The conventional fruit tarts and puddings are a bad mixture containing acid and starch, and should be avoided as far as possible, particularly by those who have weak digestions.

(186) *Wholemeal Bread (L)*

3 lb. wholemeal flour
3 heaped teaspoons
    gluten powder
1½ pints tepid water

Put the yeast, sugar, milk and warm water into a warmed basin, in a warm place, until the yeast starts to work (rise). This should be done while the mixing bowl, flour and tins are

2 oz. butter or vegeta-
   :ian margarine melted
   in the tepid water
   (optional)
3 oz. fresh baker's
   yeast
1 teaspoon brown sugar
2 tablespoons milk
2 tablespoons warm
   water
2 warmed bread tins,
   greased and
   floured

warming in the oven. It is most important that everything should be warm and that no draught passes over the dough during the actual breadmaking.

Place flour and gluten powder in bowl, mix well, and then make a hole in the centre. Into this pour the yeast. Wash out the yeast basin with some of the tepid water, add the remainder of water, and mix well. Spoon the mixture into the tins, filling them ⅔ full. Sprinkle top with bran. Place in oven (Regulo ¼) to rise. When the dough reaches the top of the tins (usually 10 to 20 minutes), turn the gas up to Regulo 6. After 30 minutes reverse the tins. The bread should take approximately ¾ to 1 hour to bake. When done, the bread starts to leave the sides of the tin, and if tapped on top it sounds hollow. Turn out and cool on wire tray.

If a soft crust is desired, the melted butter or margarine should be added to the mixing water. Omission of the fat tends to result in a very hard crust.

The gluten powder is added in order to improve texture and reduce crumbling.

(187) *81 per cent Pure Flour Bread* *

If and when a loaf with reduced roughage is required, 81 per cent flour (with no additives) may be used instead of wholemeal. In this case the dough should be kneaded before placing in tins. Proceed as Recipe 186.

* Health Food Stores sell an 81 per cent flour which is prepared by extracting roughage from a pure, unadulterated wholemeal flour. Compost-grown flour, both 81 per cent and 100 per cent is obtainable at a small additional cost.

The top of the dough may be brushed over with a beaten-up mixture, half milk, half vegetable oil. This gives a pleasant finish to the top of the loaf when cooked.

(188) *Wholemeal Pastry (F)*

½ lb. wholemeal flour
6 oz. margarine, vegetarian cooking fat, or half and half

Mix fat into flour until texture resembles breadcrumbs. Add water carefully — less water is needed with wholemeal flour, as the paste has to be drier than white pastry.

When the paste holds together, roll out carefully, and use.

(189) *Bakewell Tarts (F, S)*

Wholemeal pastry to line little baking tins.

Beat up 1 egg, and add 1 tablespoon brown sugar and enough milled nuts or ground almonds so that the mixture will drop from the spoon — a semi-solid paste.

Place a little honey or jam on the pastry, and add a good teaspoonful of the nut mixture. Bake in moderate oven for 20 to 30 minutes until nicely brown on top. Turn out and cool on wire tray.

(190) *Boiled Cake (F, S)*

½ lb. cooking fat
1 teacup water
½ teacup treacle
6 oz. brown sugar
4 oz. sultanas; 8 oz. dates; or any dried fruit and peel
1 tablespoon strong dandelion coffee
1 lb. S.R. wholemeal flour
½ teaspoon each of cinnamon, mixed spice, nutmeg and ginger

Place cooking fat in saucepan and melt. Add water, dandelion coffee, treacle, sugar, and dried fruit, and boil for 3 minutes. Remove from gas, cool a little, and then add the mixture to the flour and spices. Grease an 8-inch tin. Line with greaseproof paper, and bake for about 65 minutes at Regulo 4 (358° F.).

(191) *Hazelnut Shortbread (F, S)*

¼ lb. milled hazelnuts
¼ lb. wholemeal flour
¼ lb. margarine or
    cooking fat
¼ lb. sugar

Mix nuts, flour, and sugar together. Melt the fat in a saucepan until liquid, pour on to the dry mixture. Stir well, and press firmly into a greased sandwich tin. Prick or decorate top with fork-marks. Bake in moderate oven for ½ hour. Remove from oven, leave in tin until cold, then turn out and cut across into 8 slices. Almonds or walnuts can be used.

(192) *Flapjacks (F, S)* (If dates are omitted use half quantities.)

12 oz. butter
12 oz. demerara sugar
1 lb. rolled oats
1 lb. stoneless dates

Melt fat over low heat, mix in sugar and oats and stir well. Grease meat tin 9 in by 12 in. Spread half of oat mixture over bottom and then cover with dates which have been cut up and stewed in very little water until soft. Cover with remainder of oat mixture, cook in oven 325° F. (Regulo 2 or 3). When cooked, leave to stand for a few minutes then cut into fingers. Leave until cold before removing.

(193) *Swiss Tarts (F, S)*

4 oz. margarine or
    cooking fat
3 oz. wholemeal flour
1 oz. cornflour
1½ oz. icing sugar

Cream fat and sugar until very soft. Beat in flour and cornflour, and place the mixture in cases. Make a little hole in centre. Bake Regulo 5 (379° F.) for 20 minutes. When cold, place jam or glacé cherry in centre.

(194) *Dried Fruit Fingers (F, S)*

Wholemeal pastry
    (Recipe 188)

Line well-greased tin with pastry. Sprinkle a little mint or grated peel on to it, then half

4 oz. currants
4 oz. sultanas
2 oz. demerara sugar
Fresh chopped mint
if liked, or omit and
use a little grated
lemon or orange
peel

the sugar and all the dried fruit well mixed together, then remainder of sugar on top. Cover with thin layer of pastry. Prick top and bake in medium oven until pastry is done. Cool and cut into fingers.

(195) *Walnut Sandwich (F, S)*

5 oz. wholemeal S.R.
flour
4 oz. margarine
4 oz. moist or pieces
sugar
2 eggs
1 tablespoon chopped
walnuts
1 tablespoon warm water

Sieve flour to remove bran. Beat margarine and sugar until creamy, then beat in eggs singly and the warm water. Add flour slowly. Mix in nuts, place in two well-greased and floured tins and bake Regulo 5 (379° F.) for 15 to 20 minutes. Turn out and cool.

Filling
1 oz. *walnut butter*, 1 tablespoon chopped nuts, 1 oz. moist sugar. Beat margarine and sugar until creamy, and add nuts. Spread on top of one half of sandwich, and cover with other half. If desired, place a little icing on top of cake and decorate with whole nuts.

(196) *Frosted Icing (boiled)*
(For Christmas and Birthday cakes, etc.) (S)

1 egg-white
½ lb. demerara sugar
¼ pint water

Melt sugar in water slowly, then boil until it forms a soft ball when dropped into cold water. Remove from heat, and beat into it the stiffly beaten egg-white. Pour over cake at once as it hardens as soon as it cools. If liked, decorate by placing spoon or fork on icing at intervals and pulling away to give a rough appearance, so attractive on Christmas cakes. Speed is necessary.

SOUPS

(197) *Carrot and Onion Soup*

6 large onions
6 large carrots
3 pints vegetable stock
1 teaspoon *Vecon*

Chop and fry onions in very little fat (this can be omitted if liked). Slice carrots and add to vegetable stock with onions and *Vecon*. Cook until soft, pass through sieve, and return to saucepan to heat.

(198) *Celery Soup*

1 large celery head
3 pints vegetable stock
A little nutmeg

Wash celery well, cut into small pieces, boil in stock until well cooked, force through sieve, return to saucepan and reheat, adding nutmeg to taste. (This can be omitted.) If liked, add a little milk when reheating, but do not boil.

(199) *Celery and Onion Soup*

1 large celery head
1 to 1½ lb. onions

Chop and fry onions until brown. Wash celery well, and cut into small pieces. Place all

Nutmeg to taste
3 pints vegetable stock
A little *Vecon*

ingredients in vegetable stock, and simmer until well cooked. Force through sieve, and reheat. If liked, thicken with a little wholemeal flour and margarine.

(200) *Chestnut Soup*

1 lb. chestnuts skinned
1 large onion
2 pints vegetable stock
Nutmeg to flavour

Cook chestnuts until soft in the vegetable stock with the chopped onion. Mash or pass through sieve, and reheat. If too thick, add a little more stock.

(201) *Haricot or Butter Bean Soup*

½ lb. beans
3 onions
2 pints vegetable stock
1 cupful chopped
   turnips
1 teaspoon mixed
   herbs

Soak beans all night. Next day, chop onions and add everything to the vegetable stock. Simmer until beans are soft. Pass everything through sieve, and reheat in saucepan. Thicken if liked.

(202) *Split Pea Soup*

½ lb. split peas (green
   or yellow)
2 pints vegetable stock
A little chopped mint
   or dried mint

Soak peas all night. Next day, add to vegetable stock with the mint. Simmer until soft enough to pass through sieve, reheat, and serve.

(203) *Leek or Onion Soup*

2 pints vegetable stock
1¼ lb. onions or leeks
1 teaspoon *Vecon*

If liked, the onions can be fried in a little fat before adding to the vegetable stock; otherwise chop onions or leeks and add to hot stock with yeast extract. Cook until soft, pass through sieve if desired, add a tablespoon of chopped parsley, and serve. May be thickened, if desired.

(204) *Mixed Vegetable Soup*

4 pints vegetable stock
1 large onion (chopped)
1 small teacup diced carrot
1 small teacup diced parsnip
1 small teacup diced turnip
1 small teacup diced swede
1 small teacup diced potato
1 small teacup diced artichoke
1 teaspoon *Vecon*
1 dessertspoon mixed herbs

Fry onion in a little fat and then add vegetables. Add stock, and bring to boil. Simmer until cooked, and serve.

(205) *Parsnip Soup*

2 pints vegetable stock
1 lb. parsnips
1 tablespoon chopped parsley

Scrub and cut up parsnips. Cook in stock until soft enough to pass through sieve, or mash. Reheat, add parsley, and serve.

(206) *Summer Soup*

½ lb. spring onions
2 oz. spring onion tops (green, finely chopped)
½ bunch watercress
½ large cucumber
1 oz. margarine
A few celery seeds

Melt fat in saucepan. Slice cucumber very finely, skin included. Shred spring onions and watercress, removing coarse stems from latter. Mix into melted fat all the vegetables, and stand on kitchen boiler or on asbestos mat on very low flame. The gentle heat brings out the

to flavour
1 oz. wholemeal flour
2½ pints vegetable
    stock
A little milk

full flavour — let stand for 15 minutes. Boil stock and add to vegetables. Simmer for 1 hour. Mix flour to thin paste with milk, add and boil for 5 minutes. Serve with finely chopped parsley and a few of the chopped onion tops.

(207) *Starchless Sauce (Savoury)*

Mix 2 level teaspoons agar-agar with a little vegetable stock. Add ½ pint boiling stock, and stir until dissolved. (If necessary, stir over a low gas.) Make a thick sauce by adding a larger amount of agar-agar than usual. Stir in two teaspoons of *Vecon* until all is blended, then add a teaspoon of mixed herbs.

This sauce can be used over vegetables in place of the usual white sauce. It can be improved by adding 4 tablespoons of grated cheese, stirring until cheese has melted.

This sauce is also used in nutmeat and vegetable pies — see other recipes in the section 'Protein Dishes — with starch.'

(208) *Basic Stockpot* (for tonic beverage)

Use all the parts of different vegetables that normally are too old to eat. The mineral salt content is high, especially if you include the tough outside leaves of cabbages. Pea pods, when in season, can be utilized, also the stringy parts of runner beans, carrot tops, beetroot tops and turnip tops. *No* salt or soda may be used.

2 carrots
½ parsnip
½ medium-sized swede
1 turnip
1 large onion
1 artichoke
A few sprigs parsley
1 or 2 tough outside
    cabbage leaves or

Any vegetables in season, other than potatoes, may be used. Stainless steel or good, heavy enamel utensils are to be preferred, but aluminium should *not* be used for this recipe. Do not peel root vegetables but scrub and remove blemishes, worm-holes, etc. Cut into small pieces and place in large saucepan. Fill

cauliflower leaves
Celery in season
Dark green leaves of
   leeks

up with water, bring to boil, and simmer for at least two hours — top up with water as necessary. Strain, use liquid only (no food value left in vegetables) in soups, sauces, etc.

To make vegetable tonic beverage, add ½ teaspoon *Vecon* and ½ teaspoon *Barmene* to one cup of liquid.

BEVERAGES

FRUIT DRINKS

The acid fruit drinks, orange or lemon, can be best prepared from the fresh fruit juice diluted with water. If sweetening is desired, honey may be used.

Many of the commercial drinks contain not only white sugar, but various chemical additives and preservatives, and should generally be avoided. Many grocers and all Health Food Stores stock pure natural apple juice. Pure unsweetened grape juice can be recommended, (obtainable at Health Food Stores, good class grocers and some wine stores). Various pure fruit juices and tomato juice can be obtained in tins.

The vegetable drink (No. 208) is a pleasant and health-giving beverage.

Raw vegetable juices are very rich in vitamins and mineral salts. Carrot juice in particular is very pleasant to taste.

Carrot Juice

In the absence of a mechanical juice extractor, the juice may be easily obtained by washing the carrots and removing all blemishes with a knife (dig right to the bottom of any worm holes); then grate the carrot through the fine grater on to a double piece of butter-muslin which has been boiled, fold over, and twist ends to express the juice into a cup or dish. Other raw vegetable juices may be obtained similarly.

The free use of tea and coffee is inadvisable because of their effects on the nervous and digestive systems. Where these are indulged in, they should not be strong, and sugar should be omitted or reduced to a minimum. Beverages that may be substituted for tea or coffee include dandelion coffee. The latter is best when made from the grounds rather than the essence, and many find it more palatable when made rather stronger than suggested in the maker's directions.

The analysis given in Table 1 has been kindly provided by Messrs. Thos. Symington & Co., Ltd. It was determined from samples of their Instant Dandelion Coffee.

Do not forget the rule that drinking with meals should be avoided. Before is better than after, and ideal times are half an hour before or at least two and a half hours after a meal.

Remember that imbibing large quantities of liquids does *not* 'flush the system.' In general, thirst is a good guide to liquid requirements. In certain conditions, liquid intake must be strictly controlled as advised by the practitioner. Also, if you eat an adequate proportion of fruits and vegetables, these have considerable water content in themselves.

ONE WEEK'S MENUS: STARCH REDUCED

The following specimen menus are intended as a general guide. Substitute dishes can be selected to give variety from the appropriate Section, according to vegetables and fruits in season.

1st Day

BREAKFAST
Recipe 184 — Natural bran, wheatgerm and stewed dried fruit

LUNCH
Recipe 77 — Mushroom savoury
Recipe 129 — Boiled leeks
Recipe 122 — Chicory (omit sauce)

Second Course
Recipe 175 — Chocolate mould

EVENING MEAL
Recipe 14 — Mixed root salad with watercress

Second Course
Any fresh fruit

2nd Day

BREAKFAST
Fresh fruit

LUNCH

Recipe   70 — Cauliflower cheese
Recipe 112 — Braised carrots
Recipe 152 — Spinach beet

Second Course

Recipe 174 — Caramel pears

EVENING MEAL

Recipe 5 — Apple and celery salad

Second Course

Recipe 165 — Yogurt

3rd Day

BREAKFAST

Recipe   184 — Natural bran, wheatgerm and stewed dried fruit

LUNCH

Recipe   80 — Stuffed onions
Recipe 100 — Brussels sprouts
Recipe 142 — Creamed parsnips

Second Course

Recipe 173 — Agar-agar egg custard mould

EVENING MEAL

Recipe   6 — Artichoke salad

Second Course
Fresh fruit salad

4th Day

BREAKFAST
Fresh fruit

LUNCH
Recipe   74 – Eggs on beetroot tops
Recipe 111 – Carrots and peas
Recipe 137 – Roast marrow

Second Course
Recipe 179 – Baked grapefruit

EVENING MEAL
Recipe   15 – Mixed summer salad

Second Course
Recipe 164 – Orange jelly

5th Day

BREAKFAST
Recipe 184 – Natural bran, wheatgerm and stewed dried fruit

LUNCH

Recipe   69 – Stuffed aubergine
Recipe 108 – Sprouting broccoli
Recipe 140 – Devilled parsnips

Second Course
Recipe 176 – Stuffed prunes

EVENING MEAL

Recipe   18 – Orange salad – 2

Second Course
Fresh fruit salad and yogurt

6th Day

BREAKFAST
Any fresh fruit

LUNCH

Recipe   71 — Stuffed cucumber
Recipe 109 — Carrot tops
Recipe 132 — Lettuce, pea and carrot casserole

Second Course
Recipe 178 — Marrow meringue

EVENING MEAL
Recipe   16 — Nasturtium salad

Second Course
Recipe 164 — Orange jelly

7th Day

BREAKFAST
Recipe 184 — Natural bran, wheatgerm and stewed dried fruit

LUNCH
Recipe   83 — Spinach beet cheese
Recipe 106 — Roast beetroot
Recipe 157 — Baked tomatoes and onions

Second Course
Recipe 180 — Apple fool

EVENING MEAL
Recipe   36 – Purple sprouting broccoli salad

Second Course
Recipe 172 – Fresh fruit salad, with agar-agar custard

ONE WEEK'S MENUS: WITH STARCH

In order to avoid excessive eating of starchy foods, no more than two meals per day should include starch, and then only in moderate quantities. Therefore, if it is desired to eat bread or crispbread with the salad meal, a starch-reduced breakfast or lunch is advised.

1st Day

BREAKFAST
Recipe 182 – Muesli – 1

LUNCH
Recipe   43 – Gruyère cheese balls
Recipe   94 – Aubergine and onion casserole
Recipe 113 – Creamed cabbage

Second Course
Recipe 168 – Bakewell pudding

EVENING MEAL
Recipe 8 – Chicory salad

Second Course
Fresh fruit salad, with agar-agar custard
(Recipe 172), if liked

2nd Day

BREAKFAST

Recipe 183 — Oatmeal porridge

LUNCH

Recipe   49 — Leek, cheese and rolled oats pie
Recipe   99 — Broccoli or cauliflower with parsley sauce
Recipe 133 — Mushroom casserole
Recipe 144 — Baked potatoes

Second Course

Recipe 169 — Banana and junket

EVENING MEAL

Recipe   38 — Winter salad — 1

Second Course

Recipe 181 — Apple meringue

3rd Day

BREAKFAST

Recipe 184 — Natural bran, wheatgerm and stewed dried fruit

LUNCH

Recipe   81 — Stuffed peppers
Recipe 146 — Roast potatoes
Recipe 130 — Braised leeks
Recipe 104 — Brussels sprouts with celery

Second Course

Recipe 178 — Marrow meringue

EVENING MEAL
Recipe   17 – Orange salad – 1

Second Course
Yogurt

4th Day

BREAKFAST
Recipe 182A – Muesli – 2

LUNCH
Recipe 135 – Mushrooms and cheese sauce
Recipe 115 – Celeriac casserole
Recipe 145 – Stuffed potatoes
Recipe 98 – Cauliflower flowerets

Second Course
Recipe 167 – Date crumble

EVENING MEAL
Recipe   34 – Pear and carrot salad

Second Course
Fresh fruit or layer figs

5th Day

BREAKFAST
Any fresh fruit

LUNCH
Recipe   55 – Onion flan
Recipe 101 – Brussels sprouts and chestnuts
Recipe 143 – Parsnip balls
Recipe 144 – Baked potatoes

Second Course
Recipe 166 — Treacle tart

EVENING MEAL
Recipe   39 — Winter salad — 2

Second Course
Recipe 177 — Peach or apricot islands

6th Day

BREAKFAST
Recipe 182 — Muesli — 1

LUNCH
Recipe   64 — Shepherd's pie
Recipe 116 — Braised celery
Recipe 127 — Kohl rabi

Second Course
Recipe 170 — Bread pudding

EVENING MEAL
Recipe   35 — Pineapple salad

Second Course
Yogurt

7th Day

BREAKFAST
Any wholefood cereal with stewed dried fruit

LUNCH
Recipe 120 — Chestnut and celery casserole
Recipe 122 — Chicory

Recipe 144 — Baked potatoes
Recipe 134 — Grilled mushrooms

Second Course
Recipe 176 — Stuffed prunes

EVENING MEAL
Recipe   33 — Pear winter salad

Second Course
Recipe 179 — Baked grapefruit

Note: Those on a strict diet for weight reduction or any other reason may be required, for a time at least, to select recipes from the Starch Reduced Section only. When such restriction is no longer necessary, recipes may of course be selected from both the 'With Starch' and the 'Starch Reduced' sections.

PRINCIPAL VITAMINS AND MINERAL SALTS

In the following Tables I and II are listed the most important vitamins and mineral salts, as related to various foods. The tables have been compiled from information obtained from standard analytical tables. In cases of proprietary foods the manufacturers' analyses have been used.

I shall first describe briefly the principal biological functions of these food constituents.

VITAMIN A. — Sometimes termed the epithelial vitamin because, due to the fact that it assists the building of new cells, it is of particular value to the health of skin and the membranes lining the alimentary and respiratory tracts. These membranes and the skin are the body's first line of defence, and therefore this vitamin assists in resisting infection. Lack of vitamin A causes skin to become dry and hardened (keratinized) and hair dry and lustreless. Proneness to night blindness, degeneration of the spinal cord and interference with reproduction are other possible results of its deficiency.

VITAMIN B Complex is actually a group of vitamins.

B_1 is the antineuritic vitamin. Its deficiency can cause serious disturbances of the nervous system, peripheral neuritis, weakness of muscles and lack of appetite.

B_2 complex. — Deficiency may cause skin troubles such as dermatitis, diarrhoea and intestinal disorders, eye disorders, etc.

B_6 *(Pyridoxine)*. Until recently this vitamin was considered to be necessary to certain animals but not to humans, but it is now known to play a part in human metabolism. It has been found to act as a co-enzyme, playing a part in the metabolic reactions of the amino acids from which protein molecules are constructed.

B_{12}, the anti-anaemia vitamin, is present in liver and other animal products. It is found also in milk and milk products, and traces are found in other wholefoods such as wholegrain cereals (0.3 p.p.m.), lentils and buckwheat (0.4 p.p.m.) and in seaweed foods.

B_{12} is produced by bacterial action in the healthy human intestine (autosynthesis) but it is important to note that this process of internal production of the vitamin may be upset in various ways. A number of modern drugs, especially the sulphonamides and antibiotics, alter the bacterial colonies. Yogurt, if made with the correct culture, is said to be effective in restoring the normal bacteria.

Also, the eating of flesh foods affects adversely the B_{12} autosynthesis and therefore vegetarians should not suffer any disadvantages through not eating liver or other animal food, for they may more than compensate by absorbing B_{12} from the intestine.

ESSENTIAL FATTY ACIDS (Vitamin F). — Fats are important nutritionally in that they can provide an efficient source of energy and bodily warmth due to their high calorific value. They also act as carriers for the fat-soluble vitamins and also appear to assist growth rate and physical performance and to improve reproduction and lactation. It has been discovered comparatively recently that small amounts of certain fatty acids (in particular linoleic, linolenic and arachidonic acids) are essential nutrients. These fatty acids (sometimes termed vitamin F) are chemically classified as unsaturated fatty acids and have lower melting points than the saturated or 'hard' fatty acids. Among the best sources of essential fatty acids (E.F.A.) are corn oil, safflower seed oil and sunflower seed oil. These very palatable oils, therefore, are now being used extensively in cooking and in salad dressings.

Hard, saturated dietary fats have been implicated as possibly causing deposition of the fatty substance, cholesterol, on the walls of arteries, thus being a causative factor in coronary thrombosis and other degenerative diseases, but more recently excessive consumption of refined sugars and starchy foods is considered to be at least equally responsible in this respect, as excess carbohydrates may be converted to body fat.

Whatever the ultimate verdict on this theory may be, there is no doubt that the total fat intake should be moderate, with animal fats being generally avoided. In this book the term 'fat free' diet is relative; it does not necessarily exclude small amounts of the vegetable oils mentioned, and certain amounts of dairy produce are permissible unless otherwise prescribed. It is of interest to note that small amounts of linoleic and linolenic acids are present in butter.

VITAMIN C (ascorbic acid). — The antiscorbutic vitamin. Originally attention was called to this vitamin when it was found that scurvy among seamen was cured by giving fruit juices. Deficiency causes weakness, tendency to fractures, and haemorrhages, especially from gums. Important to healing of wounds and fractures. In rheumatism and tuberculosis there is usually a deficiency of vitamin C.

CALCIUM. — This mineral is the chief constituent of the hard portion of bones and teeth, in the form of its phosphate. It is important in pregnancy and lactation, and is one of the substances necessary for blood clotting. It affects the contraction of muscles, including muscles of the heart and intestines. It also affects the strength of the walls of the capillaries. Calcium is a normal constituent of blood plasma, and its level in blood is maintained by the influence of vitamin D and the parathyroid glands.

PHOSPHORUS is associated with calcium in bones and teeth, as mentioned above, and is also under parathyroid control. In addition, it is an essential constituent of cell nuclei and is particularly important to nervous tissues. Carbohydrates after ingestion are stored as glycogen for use by muscles as required, and phosphorus is necessary for the breakdown of glycogen to supply muscular energy.

IRON. — It has long been known that iron is an essential constituent of blood. It is incorporated in haemoglobin and thus plays a leading role in the transport of oxygen. It is deficient in anaemia. Iron is also found in cells and is associated with the action of certain enzymes.

COPPER. — A very small amount of copper (trace) is necessary as well as iron for formation of haemoglobin.

POTASSIUM, with *SODIUM*, is the chief alkalizing mineral salt and, with its strongly electropositive character, is concerned in the development of electrical potentials across membranes. Potassium, in association with chlorine (as chloride ion) assists the passage of carbon dioxide on its way via the blood to the lungs for elimination. The passage of nerve impulses depends on the presence of potassium ions. Sodium plays an important part in neutralizing acids in the blood, which it helps to maintain in a slightly alkaline condition (known as 'buffering').

SULPHUR is an essential part of certain proteins and plays an important part in the structure of muscle fibres.

OTHER VITAMINS AND MINERAL SALTS

VITAMIN D. — This is the 'sunshine vitamin' and is synthesized by the body itself under the influence of the ultra-violet rays of sunlight. Ultra-violet sunray lamps are used for this purpose where adequate true sunlight is not available. Very little vitamin D is found in fruit and vegetables. The fish liver oils (cod, halibut, tunny, etc.) are rich in vitamin D and varying quantities are found in eggs and dairy produce. Preparations of ergosterol irradiated with ultra-violet light provide a vegetarian source of vitamin D, which appears to be satisfactory for those who have insufficient sunlight. As it has been shown recently that large overdoses of artificial vitamin D preparations can cause harmful reactions, these should only be taken in prescribed quantities. Vitamin D is concerned with calcium metabolism.

VITAMIN E has been termed the anti-sterility vitamin. Its action is that of an anti-oxidant and so it serves to exert a controlling influence on a number of metabolic processes including the stabilizing of unsaturated fats; this may account for reports that it is helpful in cases of cardiac ischaemic disease. The best source is wheat germ and other whole grains and plant seeds including peanuts. It is also found in egg-yolk and green leaves of spinach, lettuce, turnip tops and parsley.

VITAMIN K assists blood clotting, reducing tendency to haemorrhage, and decreases the fragility of capillaries. Best sources are green leaves of spinach, kale, parsley, carrot tops, turnip tops, beet tops, etc.

IODINE is an essential element but is only required in very small amounts for the production of the active principle of the thyroid gland. In districts not a great distance from the sea there is likely to be sufficient iodine in the locally grown vegetables and also some iodides in the drinking water. In parts remote from the sea, especially in limestone districts, there may be a deficiency. Best sources, apart from fish, are seaweed products such as kelp, carageen moss and *agar-agar*.

MAGNESIUM in small amounts is required for bone formation. Where diet contains plenty of fruit and vegetables and thus is adequate in the other minerals, there is not likely to be a deficiency of magnesium, and the same rule applies to other elements required in minute traces.

SILICON in small amounts is a necessary constituent of hair, skin, nails and enamel of teeth. This element is found in the skins of fruit and vegetables, and this is one reason why these outer parts of the food should be eaten.

COBALT AND FLUORINE. — Cobalt in very minute traces is required for auto-synthesis of vitamin B_{12}.
Fluorine in very small traces is necessary for hardness of bone and dental enamel. Conventional diets are fluorine deficient. A wholefood diet provides the necessary fluorine and is a much better way of obtaining this element than fluoridation of water supplies, especially as over-dosage has certain dangers and dis-

advantages. Many wholefoods contain traces, wholegrain cereals up to 10 p.p.m. Tea and wine contain up to 100 p.p.m. but excessive tea-drinking is otherwise harmful, and pure, unfermented grape juice is generally preferable to wine.

Sea foods are valuable sources of mineral salts, including trace elements, hence the value of agar-agar which is prepared from a marine plant. *Vecon* is also an excellent source of trace elements.

FRUITS

It is important to remember that acid fruits do not form acid in the system, for during digestion the fruit acids are completely broken down and the residue is *alkaline*. Therefore, the acid fruits are valuable for correcting acidity of the system.

Rhubarb contains oxalic acid which combines with calcium to form the very insoluble calcium oxalate. Although some of this is excreted, the portion absorbed may tend to form insoluble deposits such as kidney stone. In higher concentrations oxalic acid is a dangerous poison. We consider that rhubarb is not to be recommended as a food. The ordinary variety of spinach also contains a considerable concentration of oxalic acid but this does not apply to the variety known as perpetual or spinach beet.

REFERENCES

McCance and Widdowson: *The Chemical Composition of Foods* (Medical Research Council).

McCance, Widdowson and Shackleton: *The Nutritive Value of Fruits, Vegetables and Nuts* (Medical Research Council).

Boas, Fixen and Roscoe: *Tables of the Vitamin Content of Human and Animal Foods* (Nutr. Abs. Rev.).

Wokes: *Food, The Deciding Factor* (Penguin).

Thorpe: *Biochemistry for Medical Students* (Churchill).

Callow: *Cooking and Nutritive Value* (Oxford University Press).

Weston A. Price: *Nutrition and Physical Degeneration* (Amer. Academy of Applied Nutrition, 1950).

B.A. Fox and A.G. Cameron: *A Chemical Approach to Food and Nutrition* (University of London Press Ltd).

H.M. Sinclair, M.A., D.M., M.R.C.P.: *The Relation of Dietary Fats to Chronic Degenerative Diseases* (Paper read at Apothecaries Hall, March, 1960).

H.M. Sinclair, M.A., D.M., M.R.C.P.: *Disasters in Diet* (Address to the Conference on *The Health of Executives*, The Chest and Heart Association, November, 1960).

Sherman and Lanford: *Essentials of Nutrition* (Macmillan & Co. of New York).

Samson Wright's Applied Physiology (Oxford University Press).

Sir Robert McCarrison & H.M. Sinclair: *Nutrition and Health* (Faber & Faber)

Franklin Bicknell: *Chemicals in Food* (Faber & Faber)

T.L. Cleave, G.D. Campbell & N.S. Painter: *Diabetes, Coronary Thrombosis and the Saccharine Disease* (John Wright, Bristol).

Sir Stanley Davidson & R. Passmore: *Human Nutrition and Dietetics* (E. & S. Livingstone).

Table 1. VITAMINS AND MINERAL SALTS IN THE PRINCIPAL ARTICLES OF FOOD

Very rich source = xxxx, good source = xxx, moderate source = xx, small amount = x, trace = tr.

Foodstuff	Calcium Ca	Phosphorus P	Iron Fe	Sodium Na	Potassium K	Copper Cu	Sulphur S	Vit. A	Vits. B complex	Vit. C
Almonds	xxx	xxx	xxx	tr.	xxx	x	xxx	—	x	x
Apples	tr.	tr.	x	tr.	x	tr.	tr.	x	x	xx
Apricots (Fresh)	x	tr.	x	—	xxx	x	tr.	xxxx	tr.	xx
,, (Dried)	xx	xx	x	xxx	xxxx	xx	xxx	xxxx	x	xxx
Artichokes (Root)	x	x	x	tr.	xxx	x	x	—	tr.	xx
Asparagus	x	xx	xx	tr.	xx	tr.	x	xxx	x	x
Aubergine (or Egg Plant)	x	x	x	tr.	xx	x	x	x	x	xx
Avocado (or Alligator)	x	x	x	xx	x	x	xx	x	xx	—
Barley	tr.	xxx	x	tr.	x	xxxx	xxx	—	xxx	—
Barmene	xx	xxx	xxxx	xx	xxx	x	—	—	xxxx	xx
Bananas	tr.	tr.	x	—	xxx	xxxx	x	xx	xx	tr.
Barcelona Nuts	xx	xxx	xxx	tr.	xxxx	xxxx	xxx	—	tr.	—
Beans (Butter)	xx	xxx	xxxx	xxxx	xxxx	xxxx	xxx	—	xx	—
,, (Haricot)	xx	xxx	xxxx	xxx	xxxx	xxxx	xxx	—	xx	—
,, (Soya)	xxx	xxxx	xxxx	—	xxxx	—	—	x	xx	xxx
,, (Broad)	x	xx	xx	x	xx	xxx	x	—	x	xxx
,, (Runner and French)										
Beetroot Tops	x	x	x	tr.	xx	x	x	xxxx	xx	xxx
Beetroot	xx	x	xxx	xxxx	xxxx	tr.	—	xxxx	xx	xxx
Blackberries	x	tr.	x	tr.	xxx	tr.	tr.	tr.	x	xx
Blackcurrants	xx	x	xx	tr.	xx	x	x	xx	xx	xx
Brazil Nuts	xxx	xxxx	xxx	tr.	xxxx	xxxx	xxx	—	x	tr.

Table 1. VITAMINS AND MINERAL SALTS IN THE PRINCIPAL ARTICLES OF FOOD—*Continued*
Very rich source = xxxx, good source = xxx, moderate source = xx, small amount = x, trace = tr.

Foodstuff	Calcium Ca	Phosphorus P	Iron Fe	Sodium Na	Potassium K	Copper Cu	Sulphur S	Vit. A	Vits. B complex	Vit. C
Bread (White)	as added chalk	x	as added	as added salt	x	tr.	xx	—	x	—
,, (Wholemeal)	x	xxx	xxx	as added salt	xx	xxx	xx	—	xxx	—
Broccoli	xx	x	xx	tr.	x	xx	x	xxxx	xx	xxxx
Brussels Sprouts	x	xx	x	tr.	xxx	tr.	xx	xxx	xx	xxxx
Butter	x	tr.	tr.	as added salt	tr.	tr.	tr.	xxxx	tr.	—
Cabbage (Red)	xx	x	x	xx	xx	x	xx	xxx	x	xxx
Cabbage (Raw Savoy)	xx	x	x	xx	xx	—	xx	xx	x	xxx
,, (Raw Winter)	xx	x	xx	xx	xx	—	xx	xx	x	xx
Carrageen Moss	xxxxx	xxx	xxxx	xxxx	xxxx	xxxx	xxxx	—	—	—
Carrots	xx	x	x	xxxx	xx	tr.	tr.	xxxx	xx	xx
Cauliflower	x	x	x	tr.	xxx	tr.	tr.	x	xx	xxx
Celery (Raw)	xx	x	x	xxxx	xx	x	x	tr.	x	xx
Cheese (Cheddar)	xxxxx	xxxxx	x	as added salt	x	tr.	xxx	xxx	x	—
,, (Cream)	x	x	tr.	as added salt	tr.	tr.	xx	xxxx	x	—
Cherries	x	tr.	x	tr.	xx	tr.	tr.	xx	x	xx
Chestnuts	x	x	x	tr.	xxx	xx	x	tr.	xx	tr.

Table 1. VITAMINS AND MINERAL SALTS IN THE PRINCIPAL ARTICLES OF FOOD—*Continued*

Very rich source = xxxx, good source = xxx, moderate source = xx, small amount = x, trace = tr.

Foodstuff	Calcium Ca	Phosphorus P	Iron Fe	Sodium Na	Potassium K	Copper Cu	Sulphur S	Vit. A	Vits. B complex	Vit. C
Chicory	x	x	x	x	xx	x	tr.	—	—	—
Cucumber (with skin)	x	x	xx	x	x	tr.	x	xx	x	xx
Currants (Dried)	xx	x	xx	x	xxxx	xxx	x	—	tr.	—
Dandelion Coffee (Symington's Instant)	xxx	x	xx	x	xxx	xxxx	xxx	—	—	—
Dates	xx	x	xx	tr.	xxxx	xx	xx	xx	xx	—
Eggs	xx	xxx	xxx	xxxx	x	tr.	xxx	xxxx	xxx	—
Endive	xx	x	xxx	x	xxx	tr.	x	xxx	xx	xx
Figs (Green)	x	x	x	tr.	xx	tr.	tr.	tr.	x	x
Figs (Dried)	xx	xx	xxx	xx	xxxx	xx	xx	xx	xx	—
Flour (Wholemeal)	x	xxx	xxx	tr.	xxx	xxxx	—	—	xxx	—
,, (White)	x	xx	xx	tr.	x	xx	—	—	as added	—
Gooseberries (Raw, Ripe)	x	tr.	x	—	xx	x	x	xx	x	xxx
Grapes (Black)	tr.	tr.	x	tr.	xxx	tr.	tr.	x	x	x
,, (White)	x	tr.	x	—	xx	tr.	tr.	tr.	x	x
Grapefruit	x	tr.	x	—	xx	tr.	tr.	tr.	x	xxx
Greengage	x	x	x	—	xxx	x	tr.	—	xx	xx
Honey	tr.	tr.	x	x	x	tr.	tr.	—	x	tr.
Kale	xx	x	xxx	xxxx	xxx	—	—	xxxx	xx	xxxx
Leek	xx	x	xx	tr.	xxx	x	x	xx	xx	xx

Table 1. VITAMINS AND MINERAL SALTS IN THE PRINCIPAL ARTICLES OF FOOD—*Continued*

Very rich source = xxxx, good source = xxx, moderate source = xx, small amount = x, trace = tr.

Foodstuff	Calcium Ca	Phosphorus P	Iron Fe	Sodium Na	Potassium K	Copper Cu	Sulphur S	Vit. A	Vits. B complex	Vit. C
Lemon	xx	x	x	tr.	xx	xx	x	—	tr.	xxxx
Lentils	x	xxx	xxxx	xxx	xxxx	xxx	xxx	tr.	xxx	—
Lettuce	x	x	x	tr.	xx	x	x	xxx	xx	xx
Loganberries	x	x	xx	tr.	xx	x	x	—	tr.	xxx
Melon	x	tr.	x	xx	xx	tr.	tr.	x	xx	xxx
Margarine	tr.	tr.	x	as added salt	—	tr.	tr.	xxx (added)	tr.	—
Marmite	xx	xxxx	xxxx	as added salt	xxxx	xxxx	xxxx	—	xx	—
" (Salt Free)	xxx	xxxx	xxxx	xxx	xxxx	xxxx	xxx	—	x	—
Marrow	x	tr.	x	tr.	x	tr.	tr.	x	tr.	xx
Milk	xx	xx	x	xxx'	xx	tr.	x	xx	xx	x
Molasses	xxx	xx	xxxx	xxxx	xxxx	xxxx	xx	—	x	—
Mushrooms	tr.	xx	xx	x	xxx	xxxx	x	—	xxx	xx
Mustard and Cress	xx	x	xxx	x	xxx	x	xxx	xxxx	tr.	xxx
Oatmeal	xx	xxx	xxx	xxx	xxx	xx	xxx	—	xxx	—
Olive Oil	tr.	tr.	x	tr.	tr.	tr.	tr.	—	—	—
Onions	x	x	x	x	x	tr.	xx	—	x	xx
Onions (Spring)	xx	x	xx	x	xx	x	xx	xx	—	xxx
Oranges	xx	x	x	tr.	xx	tr.	tr.	xx	xx	xxx

Table 1. VITAMINS AND MINERAL SALTS IN THE PRINCIPAL ARTICLES OF FOOD—*Continued*
Very rich source = xxxx, good source = xxx, moderate source = xx, small amount = x, trace = tr.

Foodstuff	Calcium Ca	Phosphorus P	Iron Fe	Sodium Na	Potassium K	Copper Cu	Sulphur S	Vit. A	Vits. B complex	Vit. C
Parsley	xxx	xx	xxxx	xxx	xxxx	xxxx	—	xxxx	xx	xxxx
Parsnips	xx	x	x	x	xxx	x	x	tr.	xx	xx
Peaches	tr.	tr.	x	tr.	xx	tr.	tr.	xxx	xx	xx
Peas (Fresh)	x	xx	xx	tr.	xxx	xx	xx	xxx	xxxx	xxx
,, (Dried)	xx	xxx	xxx	xxx	xxxx	xxx	xx	xx	xxx	tr.
,, (Split)	xx	xxx	xxxx	xxx	xxxx	xxx	xx	—	xxx	tr.
Peanuts	xx	xxx	xx	tr.	xxxx	xxx	xxxx	—	xx	x
Peanut Butter	xx	xxx	xx	xxxx	xxxx	—	—	—	xxx	—
Pears	tr.	tr.	x	tr.	x	x	tr.	x	x	x
Peppers (Green and Red)	x	x	x	—	xx	—	—	xxx	xx	xxxx
Pineapple	x	tr.	x	—	xx	x	tr.	xx	x	xxx
Plums	x	tr.	x	—	xx	x	—	xx	xx	xx
Potatoes (with Peel)	x	x	xx	tr.	xxxx	xx	x	tr.	x	xx
Potatoes (without Peel)	x	x	x	tr.	xxx	x	—	tr.	x	x
Protoveg	xxx	xxxx	xxxx	xxx	xxxx	x	—	—	xxx	—
Prunes	x	xx	xxx	x	xxx	x	x	xxx	xx	tr.
Pumpkins	x	xx	x	tr.	xx	x	x	xx	x	—
Radishes	x	x	xx	xxxx	xxxx	x	x	tr.	xx	xxx
Raisins	xx	x	xx	xxxx	xx	xx	x	tr.	xx	tr.
Raspberries	x	x	xx	tr.	x	xx	x	xx	tr.	xxx
Rice (Brown)	x	xxx	x	tr.	x	tr.	i	—	xxx	—
,, (Polished)	tr.	xx	x	tr.	x	—	xx	—	x	—
Rye	x	xxx	xxx	—	xxx	—	—	—	xxx	—

Table 1. VITAMINS AND MINERAL SALTS IN THE PRINCIPAL ARTICLES OF FOOD—*Continued*

Very rich source = xxxx, good source = xxx, moderate source = xx, small amount = x, trace = tr.

Foodstuff	Calcium Ca	Phosphorus P	Iron Fe	Sodium Na	Potassium K	Copper Cu	Sulphur S	Vit. A	Vits. B complex	Vit. C
Salsify	x	x	xx	x	xx	x	x	–	–	–
Soya Flour	xxx	xxxx	xxxx	–	xxxx	–	–	tr.	xxx	–
Spinach	xxx	xx	xx	xxxx	xxx	xx	xx	xxxx	xx	xxx
Spring Greens	xx	x	xx	tr.	xxx	x	x	xxxx	xx	x
Strawberries	x	x	x	–	xx	x	tr.	x	x	xxxx
Sugar (T.L. Pieces)	xxx	tr.	xxxx	xxx	x	xxxx	xxx	–	–	–
,, (Barbados)	xxx	x	xxxx	xxx	xx	xxxx	xxx	–	–	–
,, (Demerara)	xx	x	x	tr.	x	tr.	tr.	–	–	–
,, (White)	tr.	tr.	tr.	tr.	tr.	tr.	tr.	–	–	–
Sultanas	xx	xx	xx	xxxx	xxxx	xxx	xx	tr.	x	–
Swedes	xx	x	x	xxxx	x	tr.	x	tr.	x	xxx
Sweet Corn	tr.	xx	x	–	–	–	–	xx	xx	xx
Sweet Potatoes	x	x	x	x	xx	x	x	xxx	xx	xxx
Tangerines	xx	tr.	x	tr.	x	tr.	tr.	xxx	x	xxx
Tomatoes	x	x	x	tr.	xx	x	x	xxx	x	xx
Treacle (Black)	xxx	x	xxxx	xxxx	xxxx	xxx	xx	–	x	–
Turnips	xx	x	x	xxxx	xx	x	x	–	x	xx
Turnip Tops	xx	x	xxx	tr.	x	x	x	xxxx	xx	xxx
Vecon	xxx	xx	xxxx	xxxx	xxxx	xxxx	–	xxxx	xxx	xxx
Walnuts	xx	xxxx	xxx	tr.	xxxx	xxx	xxx	x	xx	tr.
Watercress	xxx	x	xx	xxxx	xxx	x	xxx	xxx	xx	xxx
Yeast	x	xxxx	tr.	xxxx	xxxx	–	–	–	xxxx	–

Table 11.   SOURCES OF VITAMINS
The numbers in each column show the recipes that
are good sources of the corresponding vitamins.

Vit. A	Vits. B Complex	Vit. C	Vit. A	Vits. B Complex	Vit. C
6	20	5	85	120	131
8	21	6	86	127	127
9	24	7	95	128	128
10	29	8	96	144	131
13	31	9	97	145	132
15	41	10	100	146	144
18	46	15	101	152	145
19	48	16	103	154	146
21	49	17	107	158	147
24	53	18	108	163	148
27	54	19	110	165	149
29	60	21	111	166	152
30	64	23	112	167	154
32	66	24	128	168	155
33	67	29	131	170	163
34	74	30	132	173	164
36	78	33	147	177	171
37	79	37	148	182	
39	81	39	149	182A	
41	82	40	152	183	
44	83	57	154	184	
46	84	72	155	186	
49	85	83	156	187	
58	86	84	157	188	
64	87	95	158	189	
67	89	96	164	190	
72	90	97	165	191	
73	91	100	173	192	
74	95	101	189	194	
82	96	103	197	195	
83	111	107	204	197	
84	118	108		201	
				204	

Table 111

SOURCES OF MINERAL SALTS IN THE RECIPES
The numbers in each column show recipes that are good sources of the corresponding mineral salts.

Calcium Ca	Phosphorus P	Iron Fe	Sodium Na	Potassium K	Copper Cu	Sulphur S
9	9	6	5	6	8	9
13	13	7	6	8	36	13
19	33	11	7	14	46	22
32	34	31	10	19	47	31
33	35	33	14	38	53	32
34	41	37	15-34	48	59	33
35	42	23-39	36-39	51	64	34
39	44	46	41	58	77	42
49	46	51	47	59	79	44
51	49	55	54	60	87	45
56	51	56	60-61	62	95	46
58	53	59	73	66	98	47
59	55	66	74	67	107	48
63	56	73	75	70	108	49
65	60	75-78	77	73	111	54
66	62	79	78	79	118	55
70	63	83	79	84	131	56
72	64	84	87	85	133	58
79	66	85	89	86	134	63
80	67	86	90-91	87	135	64
83	70	87	105	89	144-6	65
84	72	90-91	110	90-91	147	67

Table 111 *(continued)*

SOURCES OF MINERAL SALTS IN THE RECIPES
The numbers in each column show recipes that are good sources of the corresponding mineral salts.

Calcium Ca	Phosphorus P	Iron Fe	Sodium Na	Potassium K	Copper Cu	Sulphur S
85	74	107	112	101-2	148	72
87	75	118	116	111	158	73
89	78	119	121	118	167	74
90-91	79	128	128	119	169	78
101-2	80	144-6	159-62	128	172-3	79
127	82	152-4	169	144-6	175	63
152-4	84	163	172-3	152-4	182-182A	87
159-62	85	168	175	158	183	90-91
163	87	169	182-182A	159-62	204	113
167	89	172-3	184	167	207	168
168	90	175	204	169	208	169
169	118	182-182A	207	172-3		172-3
172-3	168	183	208	175		175
175	169	186-7		182-182A		182-182A
190	172-3	190		183		183
204	175	191		184		207
207	184	194		186-7		208
	186-7	204		190		
	191	206		204		
	204	207		206		
	207	208		207		
	208			208		

Table IV. PROTEIN CONTENT OF FOOD (Grams per 100 grams)

FOOD	Protein	FOOD	Protein
Protoveg	54	Barcelona nuts	12.9
Soya flour	40-50	Flour (Manitoba white 70%)	12.8
Cheese (Wensleydale)	29	Walnuts	12.5
Peanuts	28	Oatmeal	12.1
Cheese (Cheddar)	25	Eggs	11.9
Lentils	24	Procea bread	10.7
Chicken	23	Flour (100% wholemeal)	8.9
Almonds	20.5	Allinsons wholemeal bread	8.2
Haricot beans	20	Flour (English white)	7.9
Beef (raw steak)	19.3	White bread	7.8
Fish (varies with species)	15-17	Cornflakes	6.6
Bread, Slimcea	14.0	Peas (fresh, raw)	5.8
Brazil nuts	13.8	Cow's milk	3.4
Flour (Manitoba wholemeal)	13.6	Human milk	2.0
Bacon	13.3		

Table V. CARBOHYDRATE CONTENT OF FOODS (Grams per 100 grams)

FOOD	Carbohydrate	FOOD	Carbohydrate
Custard Powder	92	Rice (polished white)	67
Cornflakes	88	Dates	63.9
Rice Crispies	85	White bread	53
Spaghetti	84	Figs (dried)	52.9
Flour (white, 70% extraction)	82	Procea bread	50.3
Macaroni	79	Allinson's wholemeal bread	47.1
Vita-Wheat	78	Slimcea bread	46
Ryvita	77	Energen rolls	45.7
Flour, wholemeal 100%	73.4	Potato (whole)*	15.9
Oatmeal	72.8	Apples	9.2
Biscuits (average)	71	Grapes	3.7-4.6

*Note: The low-starch (carbohydrate) content of the whole ("jacket") potato is *not* fattening and it supplies valuable vitamins.

TABLE VI. — FRUITS IN ORDER OF ACIDITY

Acid Fruits	*Sub-Acid Fruits*
Lemon	Greengage
Orange	Raspberry
Gooseberry*	Apple
Damson	Strawberry
Plum*	Blackberry
Redcurrant	Apricot
Blackcurrant	Grape
Loganberry	Cherry
Grapefruit	Peach
	Pear
	Tomato
	Melon

* Dessert gooseberries and plums, when eaten ripe and raw, can be classed as sub-acid. The acidity of a particular fruit can only be an approximation, as an unripe sub-acid fruit can be more acid than a very ripe acid fruit. Also, between varieties of the same fruit there are wide differences, particularly with apples and pears.

INDEX